NEW DEVELOPMENTS IN POLYMER ANALYSIS, STABILIZATION AND DEGRADATION

NEW DEVELOPMENTS IN POLYMER ANALYSIS, STABILIZATION AND DEGRADATION

G.E. ZAIKOV AND A. JIMÉNEZ
EDITORS

Nova Science Publishers, Inc.
New York

For permission to use material from this book please contact us:
Telephone 631-231-7269; Fax 631-231-8175
Web Site: http://www.novapublishers.com

NOTICE TO THE READER

Library of Congress Cataloging-in-Publication Data:

New developments in polymer analysis / G.E. Zaikov (editor).
p. cm.
Includes bibliographical references and index.
ISBN 1-59454-511-1
1. Polymers--Analysis. 2. Polymers--Deterioration. I. Zaikov, Gennadiæi Efremovich.
QD139.P6N49 2005
547'.7--dc22
2005015495

Published by Nova Science Publishers, Inc. New York

CONTENTS

In: New Developments in Polymer Analysis, Stabilization... ISBN 1-59454-511-1
Editors: G.E. Zaikov and A. Jiménez, pp. 1-10

Chapter 1

DENATURATION OF GLOBULAR PROTEINS

J. Agrisuelas, C. Monleón, J. J. García-Jareño, P. Peña, R. Juárez and F. Vicente*

Department of Physical Chemistry, University of Valencia
Dr. Moliner 50, 46100 Burjassot, Valencia, Spain. E-mail: proclq@uv.es

ABSTRACT

The first harmonic alternating current polarography, with a selected phase angle of $\pi/2$ rad, gives structural and analytical information on the denaturation process of insulin. This method allows to detect any alteration in the composition and in the aggregational or conformational state of the protein. The reduction of the disulphide bonds and free Zn(II) gives complementary information on the capacitive contribution around the zero charge potential, for controlling the quality of the insulin samples. The Kalousek K_3 and K_4 methods also provide quick information on the structural state of proteins in solution. Proteins with disulphide bonds yield catalytic waves in Co(II)/ammonia buffer that denote the different electrochemical activity of –SH lipophilic and hydrophilic residues.

Keywords: Polarography, denaturation, insulin, albumin, lysozyme.

INTRODUCTION

Polarographic techniques provide fast information on denaturation and degradation of proteins [1-3]. The globular proteins containing disulphide bonds present a double catalytic wave in Brdicka medium that is associated with SH groups [4,5]. Those catalytic waves greatly depend on the experimental conditions [6,7] and particularly, on the number of –SH groups and their position [8,9]. The first catalytic wave, recorded at less negative potentials, is caused by the SH groups present in hydrophobic regions, while the other wave, recorded at

---

* Corresponding author.

more negative potentials, is caused by the SH groups localized in charged, hydrophilic regions [10]. Although diverse mechanisms have been postulated for the catalytic currents [11-15], the proposed mechanism by B. Raspor [16], is the complete mechanism of the Brdicka reaction scheme:

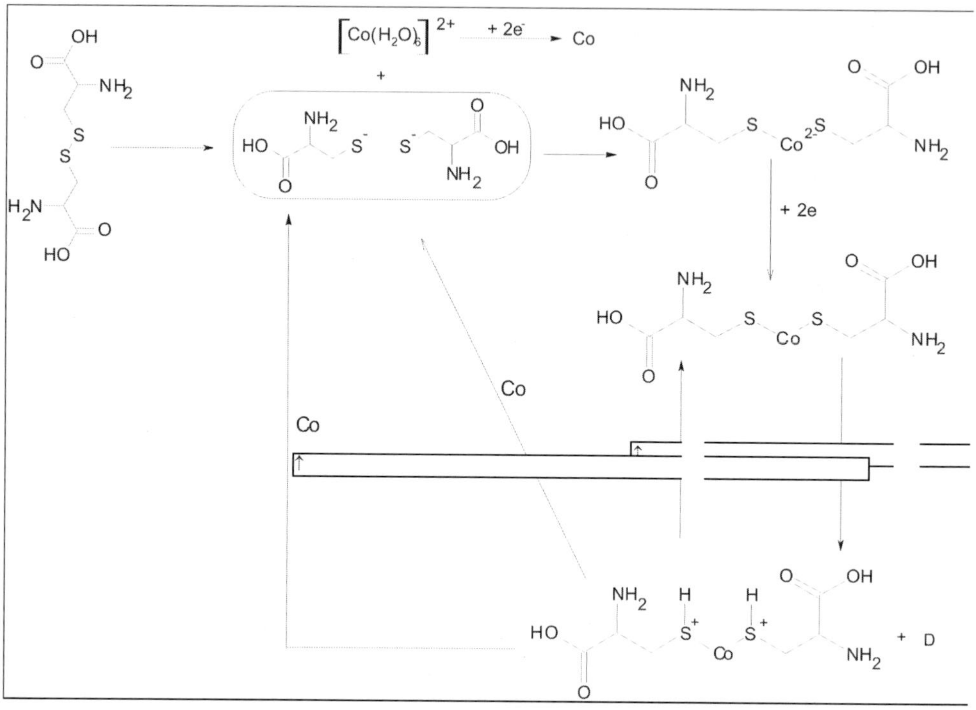

Therefore, there are, at least, three possibilities for the discharge of hydrogen, from the prewave of sodium and the two ones produced by the SH groups.

In this paper, experimental results obtained from polarographic methods of Kalousek [17] are summarized, with the aim of proving how catalytic waves in ammonia medium of cobalt are useful for controlling the quality of aqueous preparations of proteins, the electrochemical study of macromolecule-cation interaction about the macromolecule. In the case of insulin, the Zn(II) cation is an unavoidable ion, since commercial insulin preparations and the insulin present in the pancreas of mammals, are stabilized by this cation [18-20].

It is known that disulphide bonds are reduced on *dme* and that this reaction is affected by the presence of Zn(II), in excess, or by the presence of phenformine [1]. It has been proved that the biguanides are capable of capturing Zn(II) linked initially to the insulin [21]. In this paper, AC first harmonic waves with phase selection ($\varphi = \pi/2$) of the insulin-Zn(II)-medium system are also studied in the presence or absence of phenformine. In the first place, the K_3 and K_4 Kalousek methods are applied to follow the process of denaturation of the albumin and the lysozyme. The evolution of the catalytic waves with time that yield these proteins in an ammonia/Co(II) medium is studied. Next, the process of the denaturation of insulin is addressed, through alternating ac_I current polarography (with a phase angle of $\pi/2$ rad), from the reduction of its disulphide bonds. This method seems to be very appropriate in the case of insulin, since the reduction of the Zn(II) overlaps with its catalytic waves.

MATERIAL AND METHODS

AC polarograms have been recorded by a Metrohm E-506 polarograph, with a three electrodes system, by using a thermostated cell. Potentials were referred to the Ag/AgC1 (s), KCl (sat.) electrode. The capillary used in the study of the insulin had a mercury flow rate of 2.61±0.05 mg s^{-1} at -1.0V, when immersed in 0.1 M KCl solution. The drop time was mechanically fixed at a value of 0.6 s. Acetic-acetate buffer solutions of ionic strength I = 0.5 were used. The pH of the solutions was measured with a pH-meter Radiometer PHM 62 Standard that allowed to reach a precision of 0.01 pH units.

The concentration of the protein [1,21] denaturized phenformine hydrochloride [22] has been kept constant at 0.2 M in samples containing this biguanide. Amorphous insulin was chosen, since it allows the recording of better waves, CoCl (a.r.) of Merck, cystine hydrochloride (Fluka) and porcine insulin Velosulin-modified (Nordisk Gentofte of 40 u.i.) were used. Bovine albumin absent of fatty acids and lyophilized lysozyme, from egg white (98% pure), both from Sigma Chemical Co were prepared at 0.01% in weight. The mercury and water used were bidistilled. NH_4Cl/NH_4OH (0.5M) buffer was prepared. Notable microbial contamination proved non-existent in the denaturation of samples stocked at 280 K.

Peak potentials Ep, peak halfwidth $\omega_{1/2}$ and peak intensity ip were directly measured from the polarograms. n_α values were obtained from the direct measurement of the wave halfwidth $\varpi_{1/2}$ or branch halfwidth $\omega_{1/4}$ if polarograms were greatly deformed in their most cathodic branch, according to the approximate ratio:

$$n_\alpha = 90\ \text{mV}/\ \omega_{1/2}\ (\text{mV}) = 45\ \text{mV}/\ \omega_{1/4}\ (\text{mV}) \qquad (1)$$

RESULTS AND DISCUSSION

The cystine polarograms K_3 and K_4, (Figure 1), only show the cathodic component. The peak shape of the reduction waves of both cobalt and hydrogen is due to charge contributions of the acting species. The evolution of these waves allows to follow the denaturation and the degradation of the albumin samples. In the albumin, the polarographic waves are smaller (Figure 2). Simultaneously with cobalt hydrolysis, the catalytic wave of the hydrophobic region diminishes.

In the lysozyme, it is observed, that as time evolutes, the catalytic wave decreases in size, both in K_3 and in K_4 (Figure 3). In the last polarogram the discharge of hydrogen, corresponds to the so-called pre-sodium wave. The coincidence of the K_3 and K_4 polarograms indicates that anodic contribution of the pulses does not exist. The height of the waves of this irreversible process is approximately equal to that of the dc polarograms. The peak intensities of the catalytic waves depend on two factors: the reduction process of Co(II) complexed with the protein (controlled by diffusion) and other factor that depends on the catalytic activity of the protein centers.

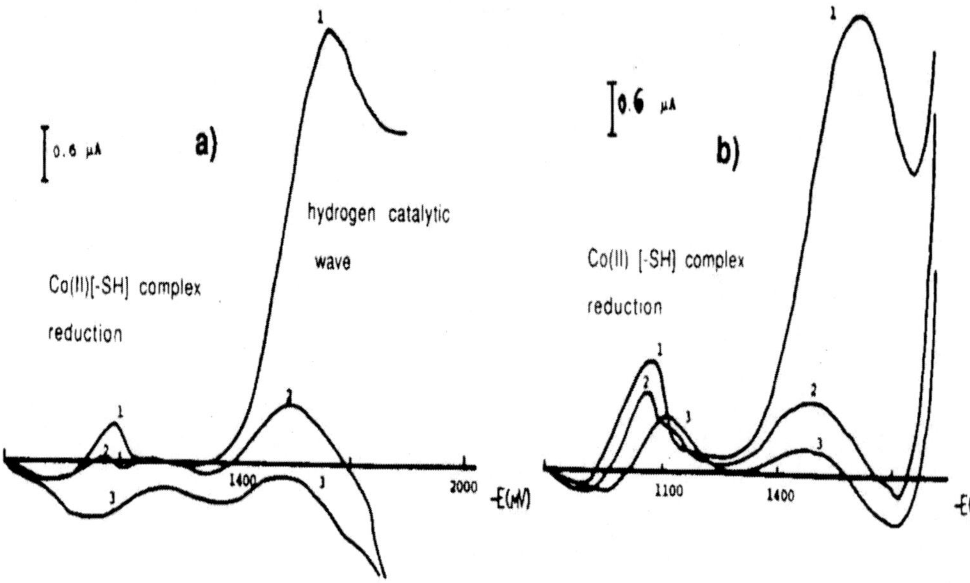

Figure 1. Kalousek catalytic waves of cystine: a) K_3 waves; b) K_4 waves. [cystine]=$4x10^{-5}$ M; [Co(II)]= $4x10^{-4}$ M; I=0.5 M; pH=8.85; T=298 K; t=0.6 s; m=0.88 mg s^{-1}; E_{pb}=-1200 mV; f_k=75 Hz. 1) 0 days; 2) 6 days; 3) 27 days.

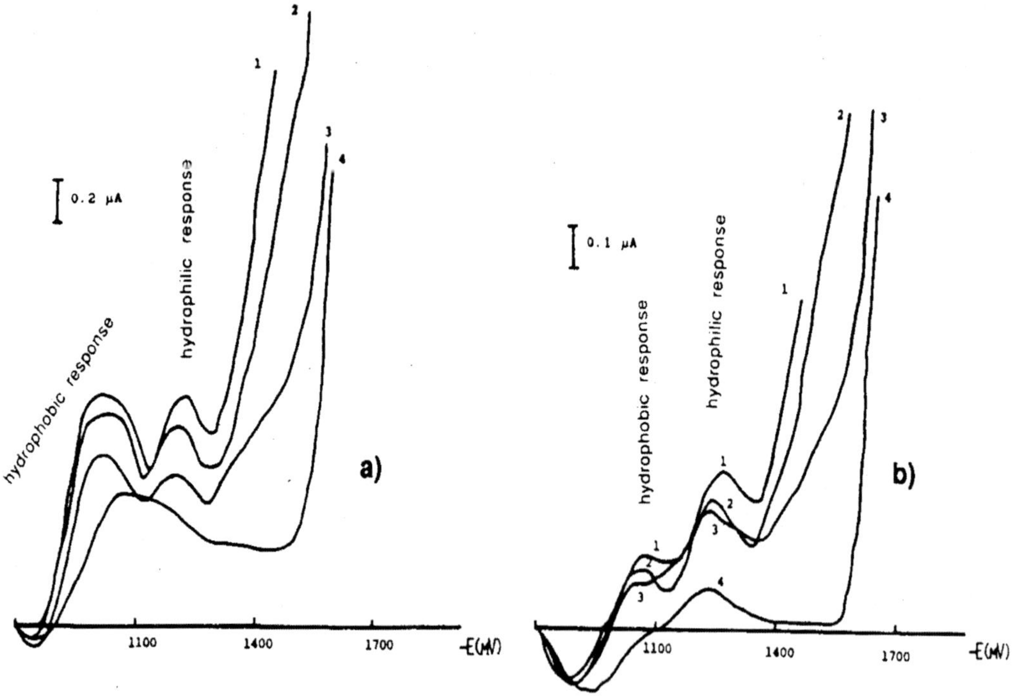

Figure 2. Kalousek catalytic waves of albumin: a) K_3 waves; b) K_4 waves. [albumin]=0.01% weight; [Co(II)]= $4x10^{-4}$ M; I=0.5 M; pH=8.85; T=298 K; t=0.6 s; m=0.88 mg s^{-1}; E_{pb}=-1200 mV; f_k=75 Hz. 1) 0 days; 2) 6 days; 3) 29 days; 4) 147 days.

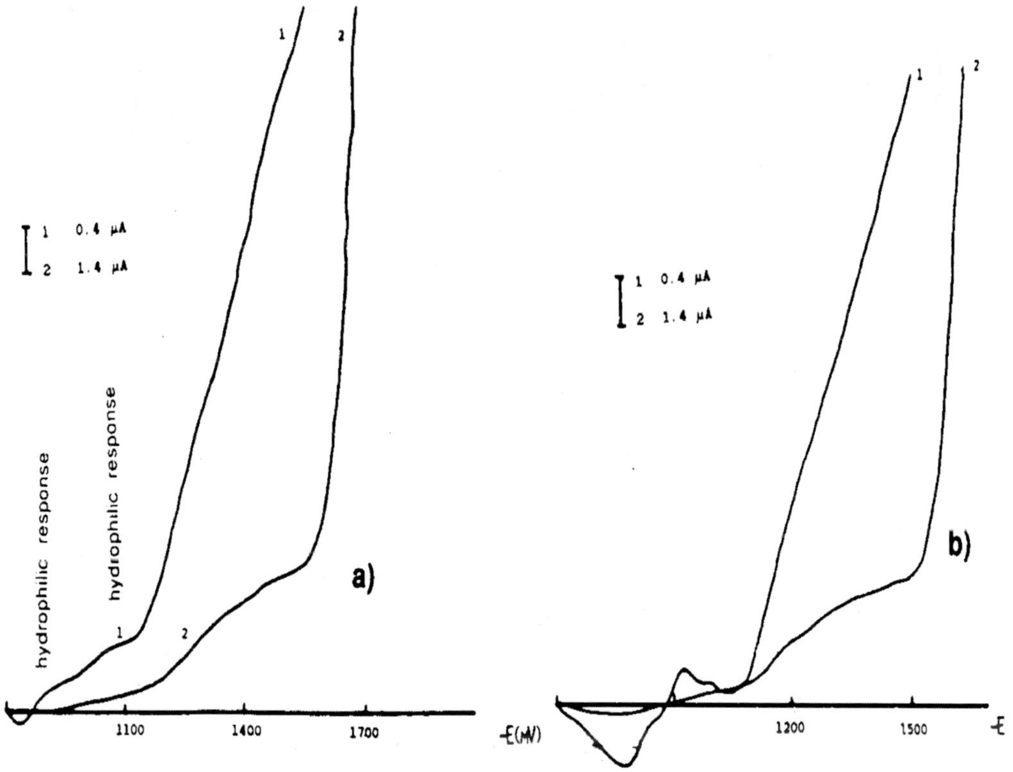

Figure 3. Kalousek catalytic waves of lysozyme: a) K_3 waves; b) K_4 waves. [lysozyme]=0.01% weight; [Co(II)]= $4x10^{-4}$ M; I=0.5 M; pH=8.85; T=298 K; t=0.6 s; m=0.88 mg s^{-1}; E_{pb}=-1200 mV; f_k=75 Hz. 1) 0 days; 2) 2 days

The insulin yield catalytic wave overlapped with the Zn(II) reduction wave. The capacitive contribution on the first harmonic polarograms of insulin is recorded in a phase angle near π/2 rad, if faradaic electrochemical processes are not taking place. The wave recorded is of the sort of capacitive curves but faster to obtain [23,24]. In every case, the ac_I (φ = π/2 rad) polarograms may be compared to electrocapillary curves.

It is known that proteins, like insulin, are adsorbed on the mercury electrode. Insulin adsorption on the *dme* affects the reduction of free Zn(II) present in the solution, since the insulin decreases the effective area of the electrode. However, this does not hinder the fact that a wave of analytical usefulness corresponding to the reduction of Zn(II) ions may be recorded. ac_I polarography with phase selection at π/2 rad, provides great information of faradaic and non-faradaic processes, complementary to other polarographic and voltammetric methods. The reduction waves of disulphide bonds were prepared. The height of the waves decreases (Figure 4) with time. This is explained on the basis of reactions of cystine degradation, which seem favoured by the direct reaction between the cystine and the mercury electrode [25, 27]. Figure 5 (c and d curves at φ = π/2 rad) involves the faradaic contribution of reduction of a new component formed so being clearly detected at φ = 0 rad.

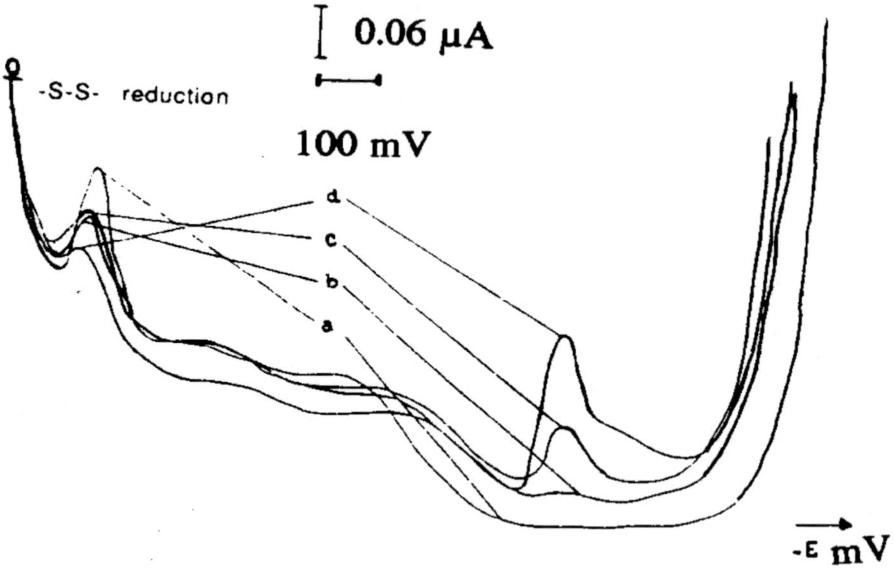

Figure 4. Time effect on the AC_I waves of cystine ($\varphi = 0$ rad). [cystine]=$4x10^{-4}$ M; T=310 K; m=2.63 mg s^{-1}; I=0.5 M; pH=5.02; t=0.6 s; ΔE=10 mV. 1) 29 min; 2) 1411 min; 3) 2878 min; d) 4334 min.

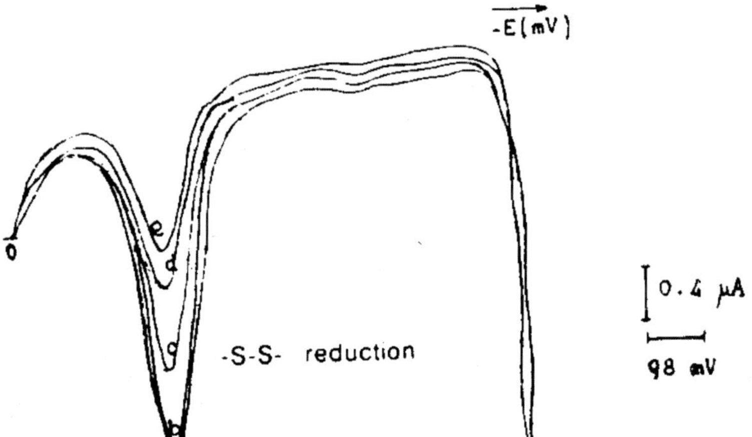

Figure 5. Time effect on cystine AC_I waves ($\varphi = \pi/2$ rad) in the presence of zinc. [cystine]=$4x10^{-4}$ M; [Zn(II)]=0.5 M; T=310 K; m=2.63 mg s^{-1}; I=0.5 M; pH=5.02; t=0.6 s; ΔE=10 mV. 1) 36 min; 2) 1397 min; 3) 2858 min; d) 4318 min; e) 8666 min.

When there is approximately 0.5 M Zn(II) in the medium, the disulphide wave remains exalted and it is clearly proved that its concentration decreases with time simultaneously with the adsorption on the electrode (Figure 6). The peak cannot be recorded when phenformine is 0.2 M, even if Zn(II) concentration is 0.5 M.

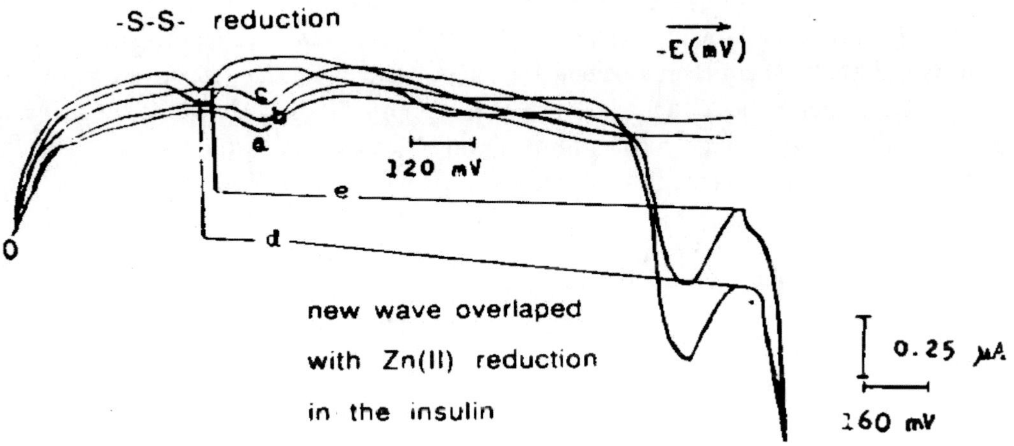

Figure 6. Time effect on insulin AC_I waves ($\varphi = \pi/2$ rad). [insulin]=6.3×10^{-5} M; T=308 K; m=2.63 mg s^{-1}; I=0.5 M; pH=5.02; t=0.6 s; ΔE=10 mV. 1) 106 min; 2) 1453 min; 3) 5833 min; d) 7209 min; e) 8674 min.

The height of faradaic waves of insulin disulphide bonds decreases, as time goes by, more slowly than the cystine ones (Figure 7). This factor shows larger steric effects in the case of insulin. Similarly to cystine, a new faradaic wave is recorded as the primary chain of insulin is decomposed [6,13]. Also, a new wave due to the biguanide-Zn complex is detected near the medium discharge.

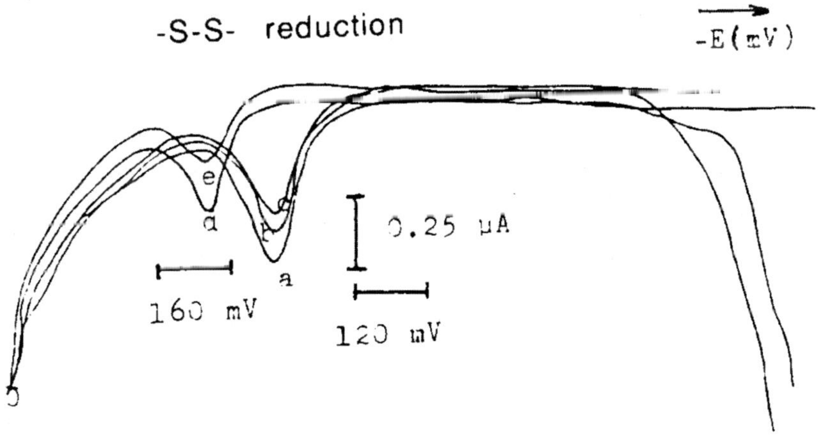

Figure 7. Time effect on insulin AC_I waves ($\varphi = \pi/2$ rad) in the presence of phenformine. [insulin]=6.3×10^{-5} M; [phenformine]= 0.2 M; T=308 K; m=2.63 mg s^{-1}; I=0.5 M; pH=5.02; t=0.6 s; ΔE=10 mV. 1) 22 min; 2) 1222 min; 3) 5536 min; d) 6959 min; e) 8394 min.

The presence of Zn(II) 0.5 M, prevents the reduction of disulphide bonds detection, that is to say, the behaviour is like it was in the case of the more crystalline insulin. The same effect is shown in the presence of a great excess of phenformine and zinc with respect to insulin. The superimposed alternating current polarographic methods, selecting a phase angle of $\varphi = \pi/2$ rad, allows distinguishing between different types of insulins. Also, its denaturation process is allowed to be studied. All insulins are adsorbed in a large interval of potentials, centered on zero charge potential, giving a zone of constant apparent capacity of double layer. Therefore, in ac_I ($\varphi = \pi/2$ rad) polarography the zero charge potential is not clearly recorded. Insulin and cystine form chemical compounds with mercury [26,27], therefore the observed denaturation also depends on the mercury presence.

During the polarographic reduction, the helical structure and intrachain bonds remain practically intact; however the denaturation of globular proteins by urea, guanidine or alkali causes an increase in the number of electroactive disulphide bridges and so in the height of the wave, compared with native insulin [28,29]. The phenformine effect is more complicated. (Table 1) Adsorption on mercury electrode and direct action on cysteinic residues yields a decrease in the height of the wave of the disulphide bonds.

Table 1. ac_I Polarographic Disulphide Bonds Reduction of Insulin $\varphi = \pi/2$ rad; t=298 k; m=2.63 mg s^{-1}; t=0.6 s; i=0.5 m; ph=5.02; δe=10 mv

buffer 0.5 M ml	porcine insulin ml	Phenformine hydrochloride ml	time min	(-S-S-) +2H$^+$ + 2e$^-$ → 2(-SH)		
				$-E_p$ mV	i_p μA	n_α
10	5	0	106	450	0.975	1.00
			1.453	456	0.825	1.07
			1.470	456	0.825	1.07
			5.833	456	0.675	1.07
			7.209	456	0.600	1.02
			7.212	456	0.600	1.13
			8.674	456	0.375	1.25
10	5	10	22	450	0.200	0.88
			37	450	0.200	0.94
			1.222	456	0.200	0.83
			1.242	462	0.200	0.88
			5.536	456	0.200	1.00
			6.959	456	0.200	0.80
			8.394	456	0.175	0.87

Therefore, selecting a phase angle of $\pi/2$ rad, gives qualitative information about the structure of commercial insulin since the disulphide bonds and Zn(II) reduction waves and capacitive contribution of AC polarograms depend on it. A previous calibration (as form catalytical waves) is needed for obtaining quantitative analytical information of the degree of insulin denaturation. However, these methods are completely useful for testing the quality of commercial samples of proteins. The information obtained from these methods is comparable with those obtained from dc or pulse polarography.

ACKNOWLEDGEMENTS

J. Agrisuelas acknowledges a fellowship from Generalitat Valenciana, Conselleria d'Educació i Ciència. J.J. García-Jareño acknowledges the support from "Programa Ramón y Cajal". Part of this work was financed by Project CICYT (MAT2000-0100-P4-03).

REFERENCES

[1] Sanz, C., Monleón, C., Vicente, F., Soriano, C. and Vera, J., *Anales de Química. Serie A, 83:3* 605 (1987).

[2] Trijueque, J., Sanz, C., Monleón, C. and Vicente, F., *Electroanal. Chem., 251* 173 (1988).

[3] Monleón, C., *Doctoral Thesis*. University of Valencia (1990).

[4] Marianovskii, S.G.: Catalytic and Kinetic waves in polarography. Plenum Press. New York (1968).

[5] Mader, P. and Veselá, V., *Bioelectrochem. and Bioenergetics, 4* 413 (1977).

[6] Kolthoff, J.M., Yamashita, K., Hie, T.B. and Kanbe, A., *Proc. Nat. Acad. Sci. USA, 70:7* 2020 (1973).

[7] Kolthoff, J.M., Yamashita, K. and Hie, T.B., *Proc. Nat. Acad. Sci. USA, 71:5* 2072 (1974).

[8] Kuik, M., Krassowski, K. and Czerniak, A. *Bioelectrochem. and Bioenergetics, 8* 141 (1981).

[9] Kuik, M. and Krassowski, K., *Bioelectrochem. and Bioenergetics, 9* 419 (1982).

[10] Kuznetsov, B.A. and Shumakovich, G.P., *Bioelectrochem. and Bioenergetics, 2* 35 (1975).

[11] Kolthoff, J.M. and Mader, P., *Anal. Chem., 42:14* 1762 (1970).

[12] Palecek, E., Brabec, V., Jelen, F. and Pechan, Z., *J. Electroanal. Chem., 75* 471 (1977).

[13] Kolthoff, J.M., Yamashita, K. and Hie, T.B., *J. Electroanal. Chem., 63* 393 (1975).

[14] Stankovich, M.T. and Bard, A.J., *J. Electroanal. Chem., 86* 189 (1978).

[15] Kolthoff, I.M. and Kihara, S., *J. Electroanal. Chem., 96* 95 (1979).

[16] Raspor, B., *J. Electroanal. Chem. 503* 159 (2001).

[17] Ruzic, J., *J. Electroanal. Chem., 39* 111 (1972).

[18] Reuscreidt, H., Stranburger, W., Glatter, H., Wolliner, A., Dodson, G. and Marcela, D.A., *Eur. J. Biochem., 142* 7 (1984).

[19] Bi, R., Danter, Z., Dodson, E., Dodson, G., Giordano, F., Hubbard, R. and Reynols, C., *Proc. Indian. Acad. Sci. (Chem. Sci.), 92* 473 (1983).

[20] Dongcai, L., Zhuli, W., Yousang, Z. and Quin-ping, *Sciencia Sinica. Serie B, 24* 23 (1984).

[21] Vicente, F., Trijueque, J. and Tomás, F., *J. Pharm. Sci., 72* 565 (1983).

[22] Noelkehjn, M.E., *Anal. Biochem., 104* 228 (1980).

[23] Doss, K.S.G. and Kalyanasundaran, A., *Proc. Indian. Acad. Sci., Sect. A, 35* 27 (1952).

[24] Breyer, H.B. and Jacobian, S., *J. Austr. Sci. Res., A5* 500 (1952).

[25] Trijueque, J., Vicente, F., Martínez, F. and Vera, J., *Portugaliae Electrochimica Acta, 9* 399 (1991).
[26] Issa, J.M., Elsamahy, A.A., Issa, R.M. and Temerik, Y.M., *Electrochim. Acta, 17* 1615 (1972).
[27] Stankovich, M.T. and Bard, J., *J. Electoanal. Chem., 85* 173 (1977).
[28] Tanford, C., *Adv. Protein. Chem., 23* 121 (1986).
[29] Florence, T.M., *Anal. Letters, B11* 913 (1978).

In: New Developments in Polymer Analysis, Stabilization... ISBN 1-59454-511-1
Editors: G.E. Zaikov and A. Jiménez, pp. 11-31

Chapter 2

RHEOLOGICAL BEHAVIOR OF RECYCLED ABS/PC BLENDS: MODELLING APPLIED TO INJECTION MOLDING PROCESS

M. J. Reig,* M. A. Sellés and T. Boronat
Universidad Politécnica de Valencia – Escuela Politécnica Superior de Alcoy. Passeig del Viaducte, Alcoy, Alicante, Spain
J. D. Zamanillo
Universidad Politécnica de Valencia – Escuela Técnica Superior de Ingenieros Industriales. Camino de Vera, Valencia, Spain

ABSTRACT

Injection is a conformation process of thermoplastic polymeric materials that, actually, has a great economic and technologic significance. Its study has supposed a lot of research tasks related with the determination of the optimal process conditions. On the other hand, the recycled polymeric materials, produced at the end of products life, are an important source of prime materials that can be used for obtaining products with good quality and low costs respect to the conventional products. Resuming both aspects, this study has been dedicated to the material study and modelling, in order to the determination of the parameters used during processing. A rheological behaviour model of the different blends has been developed that can be calculated from simple laboratory tests, and whose results have been used as a simulation parameter of the injection process.

Keywords. ABS/PC blends, rheological behaviour, modelling, cross-WLF, injection molding.

* Corresponding author. E-mail address: mjreig@mcm.upv.es

INTRODUCTION

The main drawback of using recycled polymeric thermoplastic materials is the lack of knowledge of its characteristics. The advantage that virgin raw materials offer, as far as the complete knowledge of their properties is concerned, subsequently becomes limited when these materials are reprocessed, as their properties are modified, to a lesser or greater extent, depending on the processing. The number of times the material has been reprocessed or the type of degradation the material has undergone during its useful life as a product are also important factors [1,2].

One of the most influential properties from the injection molding process perspective is the rheological behaviour of the material, and how the crucial phases of this process, such as cavity filling, depend on the knowledge and study of this behaviour [5]. The rheological behaviour assessment of the material, similar to those of the injection process, is carried out by means of the standardized test included in the ISO-11443:1995 standard, which allows the viscosity of the material to be determined by using capillary rheometers. The viscosity values of the material are obtained through this test on the basis of the shear temperature and velocity rates. These values represent a base for the material behaviour modelling to be considered in the cavity filling simulations by means of numerical methods.

Nevertheless, this test actually proves to be inconvenient due to the high costs of the equipment required, which in turn limits its use to a small number of companies or laboratories, and therefore its use cannot be considered as widespread for the purpose of materials study.

The other test used to estimate the rheological behaviour is that which is reflected in the ISO-1133:1997 standard, and which determines the flow index of the material, both in mass and volume. This test offers the advantage that the equipment required comes at a reduced cost rate, and that the results are obtained quickly; therefore this test is used widespread in order to assess the rheological characteristics of the material.

However, the drawback of this test lies in its qualitative character, rather than the quantitative character of the obtained result. It reflects a value of the greater or lesser flowability of the material under test conditions. This result only offers partial information when compared to the value obtained by another grade of the same material.

Having considered both tests, it becomes quite clear that the determination of the rheological characteristics of the recycled materials presents an added set of problems, which are not easy to solve. It is evident that the recycled polymeric thermoplastic materials reveal differentiated characteristics with regard to the raw materials due to the degradation that they undergo during the processing and, subsequently, throughout their useful life as a product.

One of the degradation effects which may be seen and which directly affects this behaviour is the breaking of polymeric chain. They generate new and smaller-sized chains. This breaking process makes the chain mobility easier within the core of the melted down material, and therefore a reduction in the viscosity of the material is foreseeable.

In the case of ABS [1,2], the butadiene phase tends to become degraded at temperatures higher than 180ºC, which causes the cross-linking of the chains and therefore the rigidisation of their structure. Their effect on the whole is an increase of the viscosity of the material.

When both effects are combined, the recycled ABS material shows an uncertain and unpredictable behaviour on the viscosity, and therefore its tendency cannot be asserted beforehand. With the aim to fulfill these limitations and in this way, to characterize the recycled material to be assessed in subsequent phases, a rheological characteristic assessment model of the material is proposed, based on the following points:

- A rheological characteristic assessment of the possible and original raw materials.
- The determination of the behaviour of the material on the basis of a flow index range study.
- The correction of the behaviour on the basis of the composition of the recycled blend.

Assessment Model of the Rheological Behaviour

Different types of mathematical models have been proposed for the correct simulation of the filling conditions in the injection-moulding of thermoplastic materials, and as a result, they offer the viscosity of the material according to its physical conditions. It is known that thermoplastic polymers tend to show a double-acting behaviour, according to their conditions. Under low shear conditions the viscosity of the material remains practically constant (Newtonian behaviour); whereas the viscosity quickly diminishes with the shear velocity rate (pseudoplastic behaviour) under high shear conditions.

On the other hand, the dependence parameters which directly influence the viscosity of the material are:

1. The temperature of the material during the process, T_m [K].
2. The shear rate that the material is being submitted to, during the process, $\dot{\gamma}$ [1/s].
3. The pressure that the material is being submitted to, during the process, p [Pa].

In accordance to these premises the *Cross-WLF* model [6] has been chosen to assess the viscosity of the material. This model still represents the shear-thinning behaviour in the same manner as the Cross-Exp model; however, the zero-shear-rate viscosity is represented by a more extensive model that is based on the WLF functional form. The Cross-WLF model is more appropriate for post-filling analysis (packing phase), because the temperature and pressure sensitivities of the zero-shear-rate viscosity are better represented. The expression of the model is as follows:

$$\eta(\dot{\gamma},T_m,p)=\frac{\eta_o(T_m,p)}{1+\left(\frac{\eta_o(T_m,p)}{\tau^*}\cdot\dot{\gamma}\right)^{1-n}} \qquad (1)$$

where:

η_o [Pa·s], is the viscosity of the material under zero-shear-rate conditions.

τ^* [Pa], is the model constant that shows the shear stress rate, from which the pseudo-plastic behaviour of the material starts.
n [-], is the model constant which symbolizes the pseudo-plastic behaviour slope of the material as so: *(1-n)*.

The Williams-Landel-Ferry expression [3] was considered to determine the viscosity of the material under zero-shear-rate conditions:

$$\eta_o(T_m, p) = \begin{cases} D_1 \cdot e^{\left(-\frac{A_1 \cdot (T-\tilde{T})}{A_2 + (T-\tilde{T})}\right)} & , \text{ if } T_m \geq \tilde{T} \\ \infty \ , \text{ if } T_m < \tilde{T} \end{cases}$$

$$A_2 = \tilde{A}_2 + D_3 \cdot p \qquad (2)$$

$$\tilde{T} = D_2 + D_3 \cdot p$$

where:

$\tilde{T}$ [K], is the transition temperature of the material, depending on the pressure.
D_2 [K], is the model constant which registers the transition temperature of the material at atmospheric pressure.
D_3 [K/Pa], is the model constant which symbolizes the variation of the transition temperature of the material, according to pressure.
D_1 [Pa·s], is the model constant which registers the viscosity of the material, under zero-shear-rate conditions, at the transition temperature of the material and at atmospheric pressure.
A_1 [-], $\tilde{A}_2$ [K], are model constants.

The use of this model implies the determination of a total of 7 parameters (***n***, τ^*, D_1, D_2, D_3, A_1, $\tilde{A}_2$), some of their values may be predetermined, either on the basis of the checked estimations by the different authors or on by a direct analysis of the material's characteristics.

DETERMINATION OF THE MODEL INDEPENDENT PARAMETERS

Once the Cross-WLF model has been selected to determine the behaviour of the material, two groups can be differentiated from the study of the significance of the model's different parameters, and the two group classification may be carried out on the basis of its dependence on the material physical characteristics.

One typical physical characteristic of the behaviour of polymeric thermoplastic materials is the transition temperature, T_g (K) determined by means of differential scan calorimetric tests. This parameter is very important in the injection molding process evaluation, as it determines a reference point for the mold open time. This temperature, as can be seen from the P-V-T curves of the material (**Figure 1**), depends on the pressure which the material is submitted to.

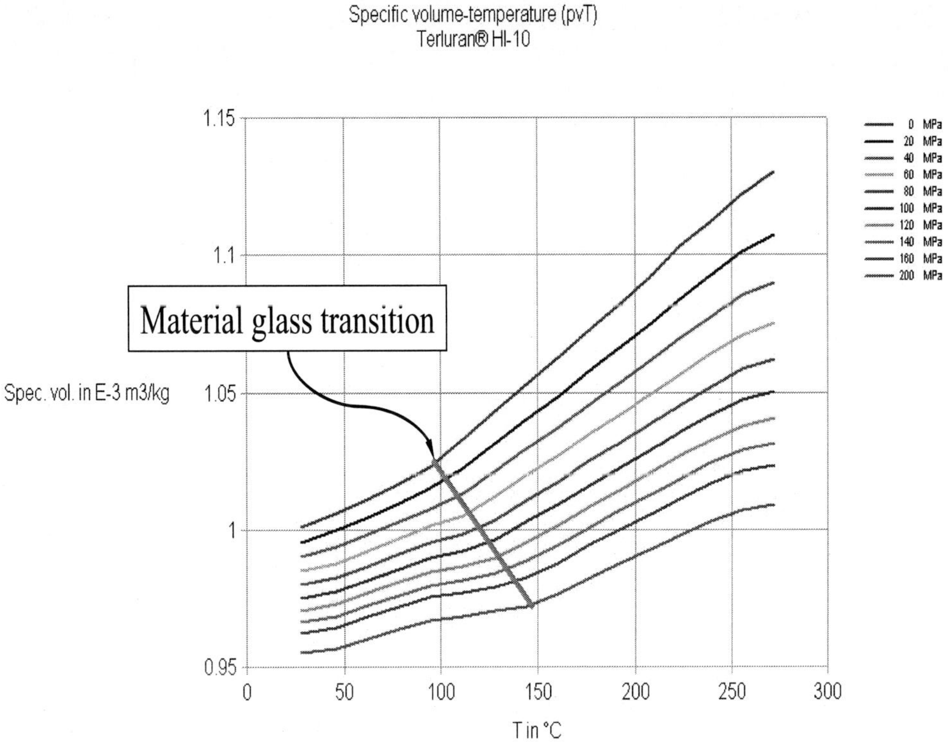

Figure 1. P-V-T curve of the ABS, BASF – Terluran HI-10 grade.

However, despite this dependence, if we consider the data relative to the virgin ABS offered by different manufacturers in their polymeric material data bases (BASF, Bayer, Dow Plastics, GE), we can conclude that:

- The ABS transition temperature varies within a very limited range at atmospheric pressure:

  $T_g = 95°C \div 115°C$

  $\overline{T}_g = 105\,°C$

- The variation of the transition temperature as far as the material pressure is concerned, remains constant and independent of the transition temperature value at atmospheric pressure:
-

$$\frac{\partial T_g}{\partial p} \cong 0,25 \text{ K/MPa}$$

These set values may be generically extrapolated to the set of ABS recycled materials if we consider that:

- Recycled materials come from any of the commercially available ranges and are characterized by the aforementioned values.
- In view of an eventual mixture of different ABS grades, the final temperature will not be affected given the limited range of these parameters.

According to Williams-Landel-Ferry model (WLF), the $\boldsymbol{D_2}$, $\boldsymbol{D_3}$ parameters reflect the behaviour of the material with regard to the transition phenomenon, so they may be directly associated with the transition temperature values and also to the variation of the transition temperature with pressure.

In the study of the WLF model [3], it has been deduced that the parameter $\boldsymbol{\tilde{A}_2}$, in the polymers case, presents a constant value, so it may be considered as a constant of the model. Therefore, the following differentiation among the parameters of the model is proposed:

- The independent parameters, $\boldsymbol{D_2}$, $\boldsymbol{D_3}$, $\boldsymbol{\tilde{A}_2}$, which are related to the intrinsic behaviour of the material, are either basically dependent on the ABS as generic material, or are completely independent.
- The dependent parameters, $\boldsymbol{n}$, $\boldsymbol{\tau^*}$, $\boldsymbol{D_1}$, $\boldsymbol{A_1}$, whose values are particular to each ABS grade.

According to the previous considerations, the following values are adopted for the independent parameters of the ABS recycled material:

$$\tilde{A}_2 = 51{,}6\,\mathrm{K}$$
$$D_2 = \overline{T}_g = 105\,^{\circ}\mathrm{C} = 378{,}15\,\mathrm{K}$$
$$D_3 = \frac{\partial T_g}{\partial p} = 0{,}25\cdot 10^{-6}\ \mathrm{K/Pa}$$

with which the WLF model of the proposed recycled ABS remains as follows:

$$\eta_o(T_m, p) = \begin{cases} D_1 \cdot e^{\left(-\frac{A_1\cdot(T-\tilde{T})}{A_2+(T-\tilde{T})}\right)}, & \text{if } T_m \geq \tilde{T} \\ \infty, & \text{if } T_m < \tilde{T} \end{cases}$$
$$A_2 = 51{,}6 + 0{,}25\cdot 10^{-6}\cdot p$$
$$\tilde{T} = 378{,}15 + 0{,}25\cdot 10^{-6}\cdot p \tag{3}$$

DETERMINATION OF THE MODEL'S DEPENDENT PARAMETERS

In order to determine the dependent parameters of the Cross-WLF model of the recycled material, a comparative model has been considered taking the reference on the virgin materials within the available commercial grades, which may be applied to any recycled

ABS. The proposal of a rheological behaviour model of a recycled material is only feasible by means of capillary rheometer tests, the proposed methodology of this rheological behaviour assessment needs a set of simplifications to be introduced, allowing a relation to be established between raw and recycled materials. The methodology proposed is structured according to the diagram shown in **Figure 2**.

The initial stage is based on the collection of rheological information of the virgin raw materials which are considered for the elaboration of the model. To this effect, the following data are required:

- Melt Flow Index [MFI] of the material evaluated according to the ISO-1133:1997 standard. In the ABS case, this test must be carried out with a 10 kg load and with a mass temperature of 220 ºC.
- Material viscosity data obtained according to the ISO-11443:1995 standard, and presented on the basis of the shear temperature and velocity rates. With a view to the results being significant for their evaluation, it is important that the interval of shear velocity of the results are within the range [100÷10000 s^{-1}], which corresponds to the usual values reached in the injection molding process.

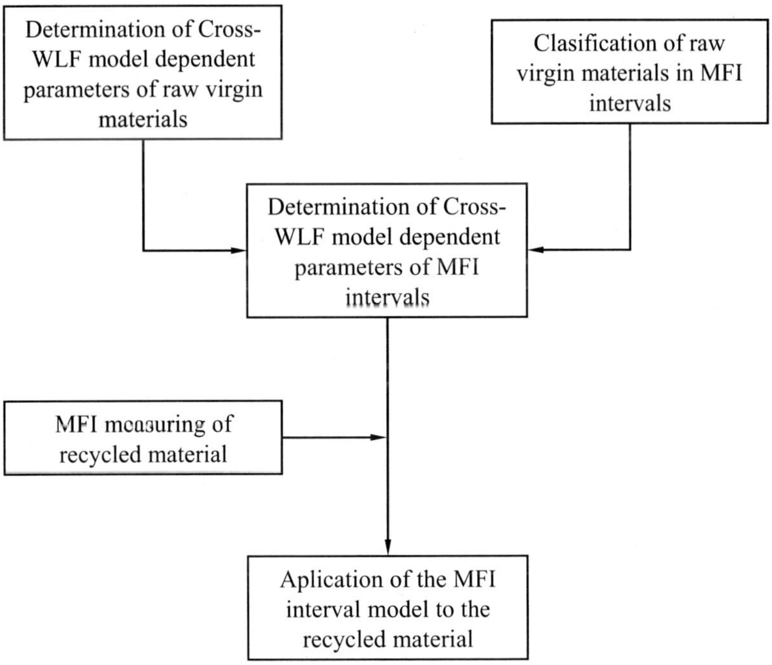

Figure 2. Diagram for the determination of the dependent parameters of the Cross-WLF model of the recycled material.

With the data-listing related to the melt flow index of the materials, it is important to determine a set of intervals to assess the recycled material model, since the definition of the model for each type of recycled material would prove time-consuming, and at the same time, inaccurate. This model discretization is countersigned by the fact that small variations in the material viscosity do not affect the processing effects (basically pressure) to a great extent, which, in this set of conditions, allows the rheological behaviour of the recycled materials to be approached [4].

In order to achieve an appropriate correlation of results, the total number of data on virgin materials must be sufficiently high and varied. In this particular case a total of 43 ABS ranges have been considered, belonging to 3 manufacturers (BASF, Bayer, GE). As a result of the analysis, the different ABS ranges are seen to have a wide variation range of MFI, and within whose limits the work ranges must be established:

- Minimal MFI: 4 gr/10 min.
- Maximal MFI: 80 gr/10 min.

Given that the MFI is actually the indicator of a viscosity value measured under the material shear temperature and velocity conditions, the MFI interval subdivision for the modeling must be established according to a logarithmic scale (exactly as the viscosity-shear rate curves of polymeric materials are shown).

Trying to accommodate possible materials with MFI indices outside the range assessed on the samples, the minimum and maximum values of the total range considered are:

- Minimal sample MFI:: 3 gr/10 min. [ln(MFI) = 0,92]
- Maximal sample MFI: 90 gr/10 min. [ln(MFI) = 4,50]

According to this criterion, the resulting ranges proposed for the ABS are as follows:

A) Interval 1: ABS with high viscosity.
Minimum value: 2,5 gr/10 min. [ln(MFI) = 0,92]
Maximum value: 9 gr/10 min. [ln(MFI) = 2,20]

B) Interval 2: ABS with medium viscosity.
Minimum value: 9 gr/10 min. [ln(MFI) = 2,20]
Maximum value: 30 gr/10 min. [ln(MFI) = 3,40]

C) Interval 3: ABS with low viscosity.
Minimum value: 30 gr/10 min. [ln(MFI) = 3,40]
Maximum value: 90 gr/10 min. [ln(MFI) = 4,50]

Data relative to the viscosity of the material provided by the different manufacturers* have been collected independently from the classification of ranges in each of the proposed MFI intervals, and also the Cross-WLF models corresponding to each range have been calculated. As a result of the former classification, the virgin raw materials are classified according to Table 1.

The following aspects to obtain these models have been considered:

- The independent parameters of the proposed Cross-WLF model have been maintained for every model: $\boldsymbol{D_2}$, $\boldsymbol{D_3}$, $\boldsymbol{\tilde{A}_2}$.

---

* Obtained from the CAMPUS© data base provided by the BASF and Bayer manufacturers, and from the data base from the GE web site (www.geplastics.com).

- In order to determine the remaining parameters: $\boldsymbol{n}$, $\boldsymbol{\tau^*}$, $\boldsymbol{D_1}$, $\boldsymbol{A_1}$, the Chi-squared function minimization criterion has been applied:

$$\text{minimun} \sum_i \left(\frac{\left(x_{i\ measured} - x_{i\ estimated}\right)^2}{x_{i\ estimated}} \right) \tag{4}$$

solved through the mathematical analysis software.

In this way a correlation value is guaranteed between the estimated and real data which is close to 1, as well as guaranteeing a minimization in the probability of the Chi-squared Test.

- The pressure considered for the assessment of the models is taken as zero, just as it corresponds to the material test case by means of a capillary rheometer and/or a plate rheometer.

Table 1. Summary of ABS Grades Classification

Manufacturer	Interval 1	Interval 2	Interval 3
BASF	6	6	2
Bayer	1	4	3
GE	7	9	5
Total No. of grades	14	19	10

Once the values are calculated and classified according to the stated MFI intervals, the Cross-WLF model parameters have been determined for each interval. This calculation has been based on the following set of premises, based on the physical meaning that the different parameters have within the Cross-WLF model, which define the proposed criterion in this particular work for the recycled material modeling from a rheological point of view:

- According to the Cross model, the $\boldsymbol{n}$ parameter reflects the slope of the shear viscosity-velocity curve in the pseudo-plastic behaviour interval.

Given the similarity of the values for the different ranges, the $\boldsymbol{n}$ parameter of the model is determined as the arithmetic mean of the $\boldsymbol{n_i}$ parameters of each range of the considered interval.

$$n = \frac{\sum_{i=1}^{m} n_i}{m} \tag{5}$$

where $\boldsymbol{m}$ is the number of ranges belonging to the interval.

- The $\boldsymbol{\tau^*}$ parameter shows the shear tension rate which represents the boundary between the Newtonian behaviour and the pseudo-plastic behaviour. In this case, the dispersion of values is stressed when considering the numerical value as opposed to the logarithmic value of the set of parameters. So, the $\boldsymbol{\tau^*}$ parameter of the interval model is calculated as follows:

$$\log\left(\tau^*\right)=\frac{\sum_{i=1}^{m}\log\left(\tau_i^*\right)}{m} \tag{6}$$

- The D_1 parameter indicates the material viscosity under zero-shear-rate conditions at the transition temperature of the material and at atmospheric pressure. In this case, the dispersion of values is also stressed when considering the numerical value as opposed to the logarithmic value of the set of parameters. Therefore, the determination of the D_1 parameter of the interval model considered is:

$$\log\left(D_1\right)=\frac{\sum_{i=1}^{m}\log\left(D_{1_i}\right)}{m} \tag{7}$$

- Finally, the A_1 parameter of the model shows similar numerical values for all the ranges of each interval. The determination of the A_1 parameter of the interval model considered is:

$$A_1=\frac{\sum_{i=1}^{m}A_{1_i}}{m} \tag{8}$$

As a result of applying the previous expressions, the dependent parameters of the models of each interval are as indicated in Table 2:

Table 2. Cross-wlf Model Parameters of the Different ABS Intervals

	n	τ*	D_1	D_2	D_3	A_1	$\tilde{A}_2$
MFI Interval	-	Pa	Pa·s	K	K/Pa	-	K
[2,5 - 9[	0,2463	91296	$1{,}48007\cdot10^{13}$	378,15	$2{,}50\cdot10^{-7}$	29,97353	51,6
[9 - 30[	0,2582	81484	$2{,}9315\cdot10^{12}$	378,15	$2{,}50\cdot10^{-7}$	29,18832	51,6
[30 - 100[	0,25691	85420	$1{,}62078\cdot10^{12}$	378,15	$2{,}50\cdot10^{-7}$	29,47763	51,6

The viscosity graph corresponding to the resulting model parameters is shown in **Figure 3**.

As a comparative result, the graphs of the different viscosity intervals are shown along with the resulting graph of the model corresponding to each of them (**Figure 4** to **Figure 6**).

As the graphs and the calculated data show, the adjustments of each interval modeling sufficiently and reliably adjust to each of the ranges. From the cavity-filling phase perspective, in which the shear rate range reached varies between 100 and 10000 s^{-1}, the interval approximation is appropriate enough.

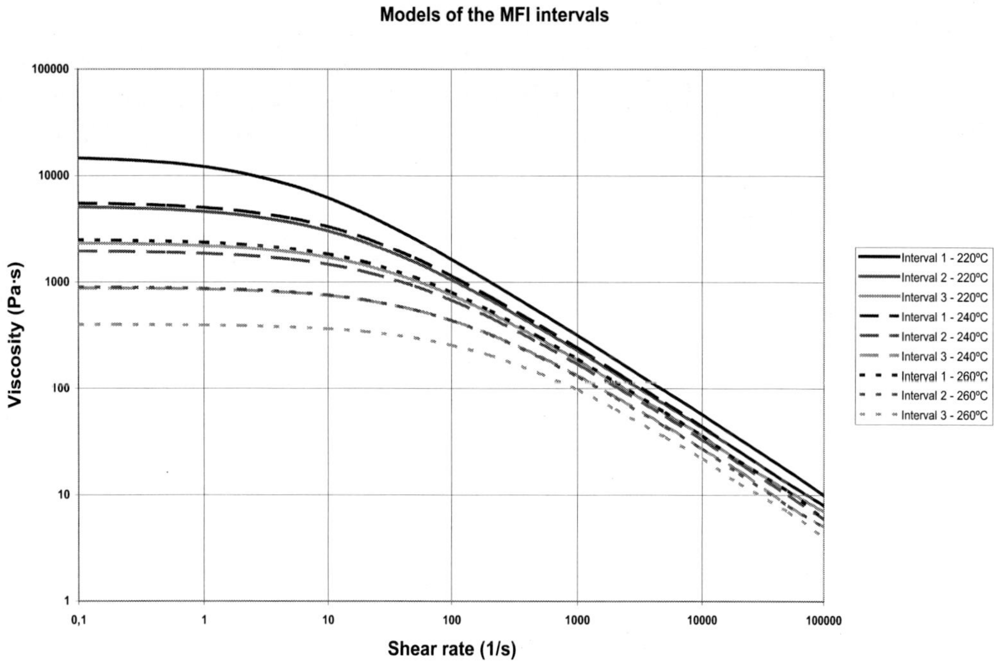

Figure 3. Viscosity graphs of the different MFI interval models (p = 0 Pa).

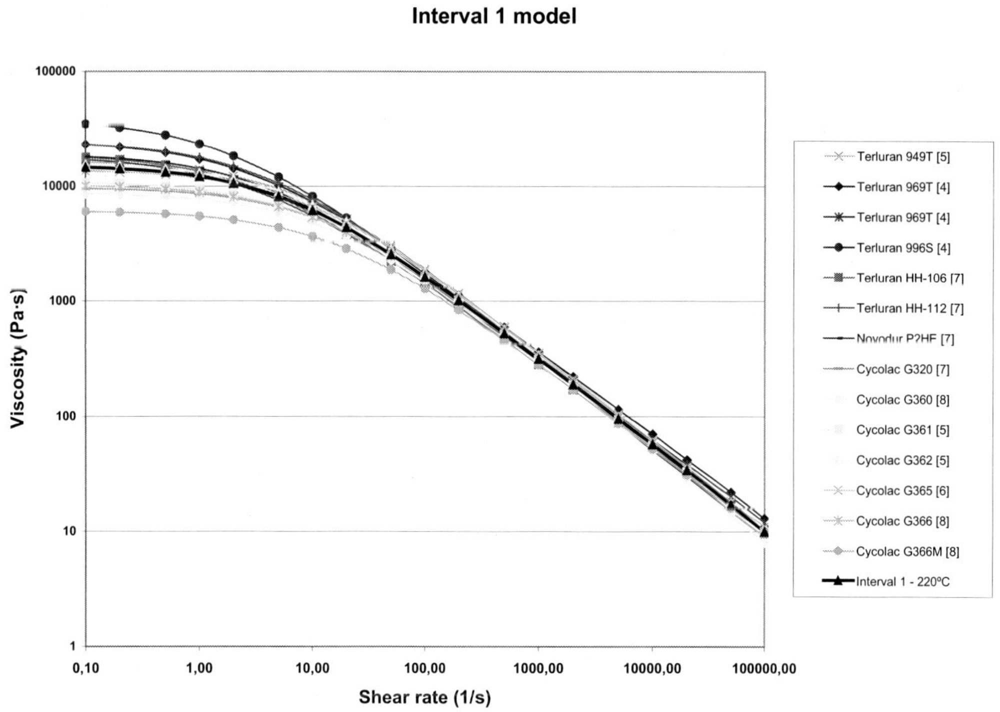

Figure 4. Viscosity graphs of the materials of interval 1 (T = 220 °C, p = 0 Pa).

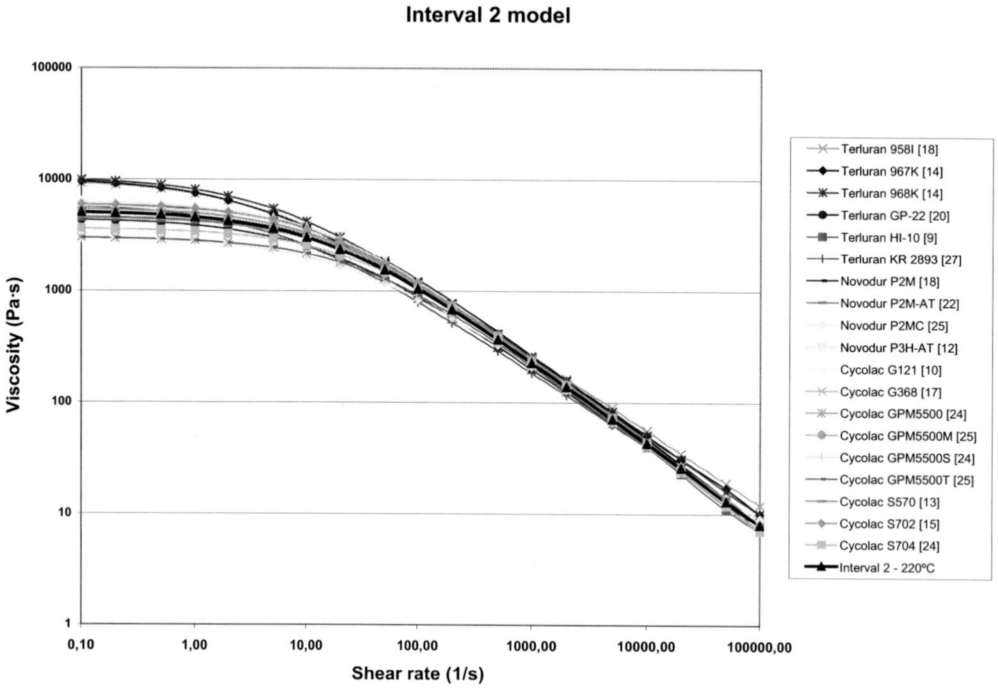

Figure 5. Viscosity graphs of the materials of interval 2 (T = 220 ºC, p = 0 Pa).

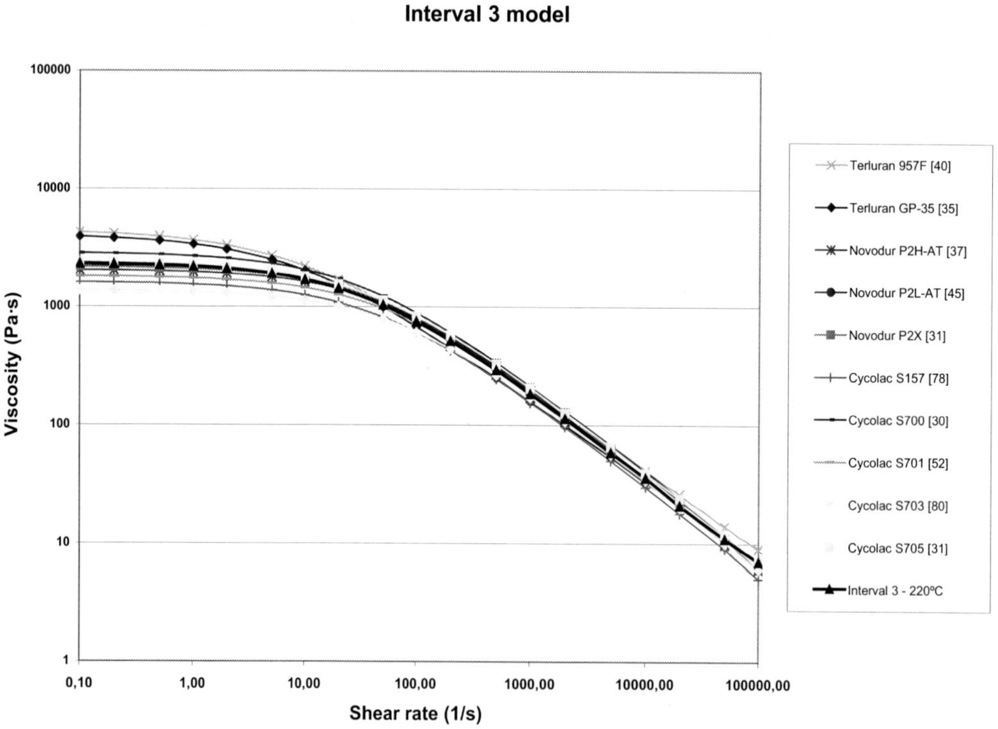

Figure 6. Viscosity graphs of the materials of interval 3 (T = 220 ºC, p = 0 Pa).

EXPERIMENTAL VALIDATION OF THE RHEOLOGICAL BEHAVIOUR MODEL

In order to validate the proposed models regarding the behaviour modeling of rheological results, a set of samples which correspond to three recycled ABS compositions, with the addition of PC, have been prepared. The material used in this particular study has been obtained from used housings to protect injection-processed computer components; while the PC recycled material has been obtained from waste CD´s. All of them are from an unknown source, which means that the grade used as a raw material cannot be determined. The pellets preparation has been as follows:

- Crushed in a pulverizing mill.
- Base materials were mixed in a spinning drum, with the composition in accordance to the weight ratio considered for the different blends.
- Materials were extruded conventionally in a single-screw extruder at a temperature of 230 °C at the pumping zone and nozzle stage.

The compositions considered in this particular study are:

A) Blend A. ABS: 100%.
B) Blend B. ABS: 95% + PC: 5%.
C) Blend C. ABS: 95% + PC: 10%.

By means of the standardised test used to determine the flow index of the material, the MFI index of the different blends has been determined, and the following results were obtained:

D) Blend A. MFI: 52 gr/10 min.
E) Blend B. MFI: 58 gr/10 min.
F) Blend C. MFI: 63 gr/10 min.

The following observations can be emphasized in accordance to these results:

Such a high flow of all the blends confirm that the ABS (original raw material) used corresponds to a material which is ideal for injection molding process.

- These results can allow us to assume that the degradation of the material has not been excessive after the various stages of processing, usage and material recovery.
- The addition of PC brings about small increases in the MFI index; the greater the index, the greater PC content. This is contradictory given that the PC viscosity is higher than the ABS viscosity.
- As far as the modeling by means of the process proposed in this chapter is concerned, the model corresponding to interval 3 (high flow material) would be applied to all the blends, and the small difference in the flow indices in relation to the results obtained by simulation, must be taken into account.

With a view to contrast the model proposed for the material with the real behaviour of the material, a standardized test has been carried out to determine the viscosity of the different blends by means of the capillary rheometer. Measurements have been taken with a 20 kN Rheoflixer MT capillary rheometer, in accordance to the following initial test conditions:

- Temperature of the material: 220 – 240 – 260 ºC
- Diameter of the used capillary die: 1 mm
- Capillary lengths: 10 – 20 – 30 mm
- Apparent shear velocities: 100 – 200 – 500 – 1000 – 2000 – 5000 - 10000 s^{-1}

The results obtained at a temperature of 260ºC during the test are irregular, and allow us to assume that the material suffers a degradation which difficult the measurements. Therefore, the measuring temperatures which are considered as a second term are as follows:

- Temperature of the material: 220 – 230 – 240 ºC

The results obtained have been corrected by using the Bagley and Weissenberg-Rabinowitsch corrections (linear model) to obtain the real viscosity values as opposed to the shear rate and temperature. By following the same procedure as in the virgin materials case, the rheological behaviour Cross-WLF model has been assessed, by applying the same conceptions as in that particular case.

- The independent parameters of the Cross-WLF model, proposed in this particular model, have been maintained: $\boldsymbol{D_2, D_3, \tilde{A}_2}$.
- To determine the remaining parameters: $\boldsymbol{n, \tau^*, D_1, A_1}$, the Chi-squared function minimization criterion has been applied:

$$\text{minimun} \sum_i \left(\frac{\left(x_{i\ measured} - x_{i\ estimated} \right)^2}{x_{i\ estimated}} \right)$$

  solved by means of the mathematical analysis software MathCAD® 2000 Professional**. In this way a correlation value between estimated data and the real data is guaranteed, which are close to the unit, as well as guaranteeing a minimization in the probability of the Chi-squared Test.
- The pressure value for the assessment of the models is taken as zero, just as it corresponds to the material test case by means of a capillary rheometer and/or a plate rheometer.

The Cross-WLF model parameters which correspond to the different material blends are shown in **Table 3**.

** MathCAD 2000 Professional is a registered trade mark by MathSoft, Inc.

Table 3. Cross-WLF Model Parameters of the Different Material Mixtures

	n	τ^*	D_1	D_2	D_3	A_1	$\tilde{A}_2$
Mixture	-	Pa	Pa·s	K	K/Pa	-	K
A	0,20187	109758	$3{,}5001\cdot10^{10}$	378,15	$2{,}50\cdot10^{-7}$	24,398	51,6
B	0,22733	89038,8	$2{,}4516\cdot10^{12}$	378,15	$2{,}50\cdot10^{-7}$	30,46101	51,6
C	0,25256	73143,9	$6{,}2731\cdot10^{12}$	378,15	$2{,}50\cdot10^{-7}$	31,99459	51,6

The viscosity graph which corresponds to the resulting model parameters of each blend is shown in **Figure 7**.

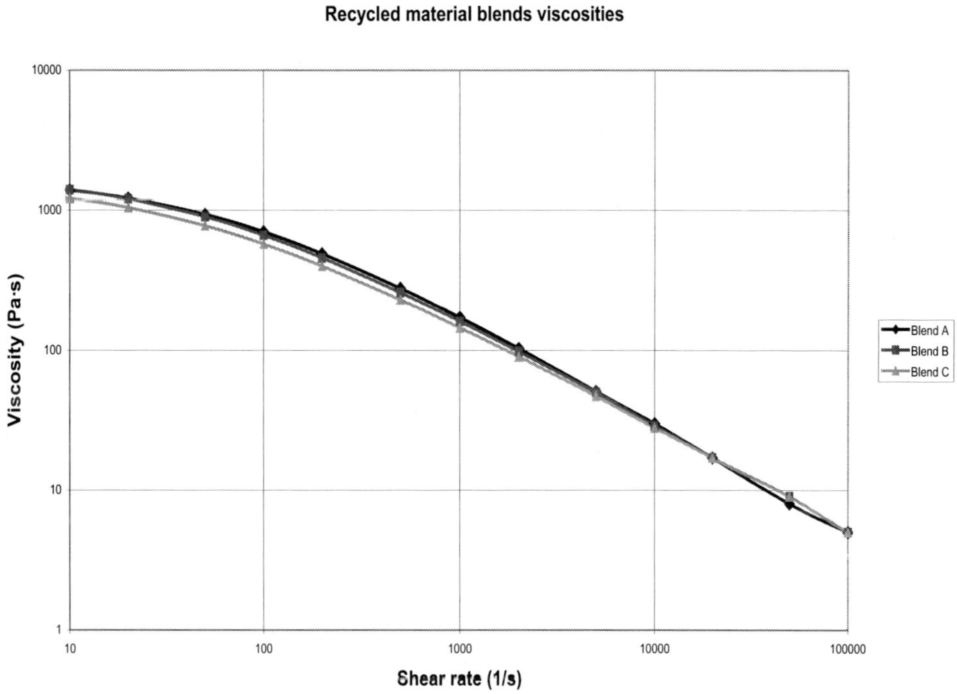

Figure 7. Graphs of the viscosity of the material mixtures (T = 220 ºC, p = 0 Pa).

These results confirm that the rheological behaviour improves when PC is added to the mixture of recycled material, which makes mold filling easier (low injection pressure).

Correction of Interval Model Parameters

As is seen from the results obtained for the 3 considered blends, the Cross-WLF model must be corrected as far as the PC content is concerned, in order to take into account the effects of the addition of determined amounts of this material, improving its flow [1,2].

By assessing the variation in the Cross-WLF model parameters, obtained experimentally and which correspond to the increase in the PC content in the blend, the proportionality factor between the ***n***, ***τ****, ***ln(D₁)*** and ***A₁*** parameters of each of the blends (A (PC 0%); B (PC 5%); C (PC 10%)) has been established. These proportionality factors are reflected in Table 4 and **Figure 8** to **Figure 11**.

Table 4. Proportionality Factors of the Cross-WLF Model Parameters in Relation to the PC Content in the Blend with Regard to Blend A (PC 0%)

	n	τ*	ln(D_1)	A_1
Blend A	**1,0000**	**1,0000**	**1,0000**	**1,0000**
Blend B	1,1261	0,8112	1,1750	1,2485
Blend C	1,2511	0,6664	1,2137	1,3114

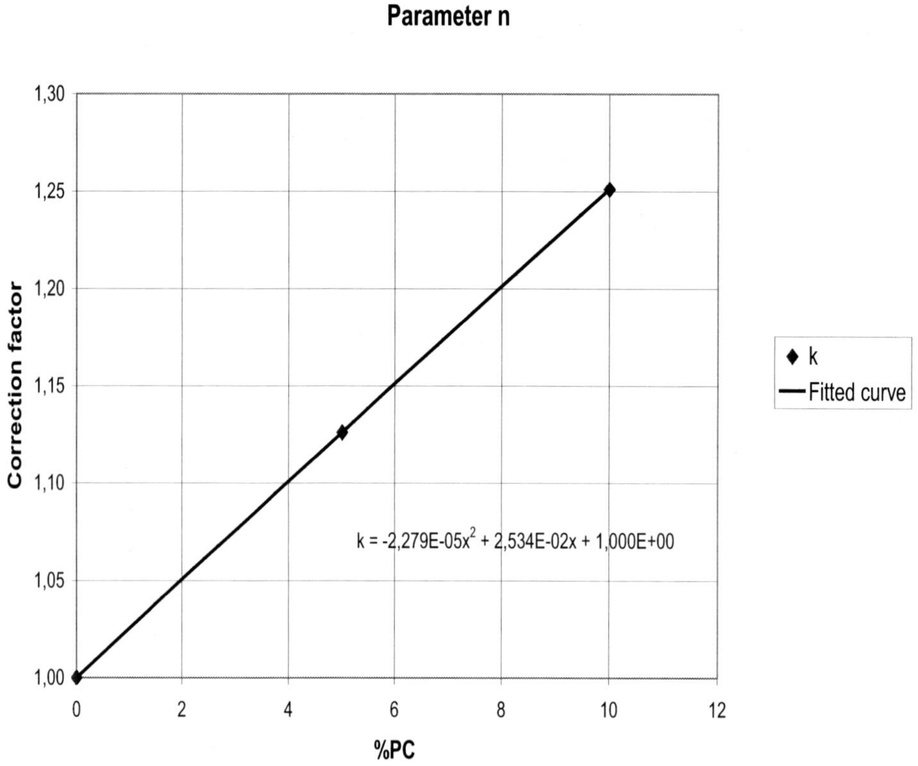

Figure 8. Correction factor graph of the n parameter in relation to the PC content.

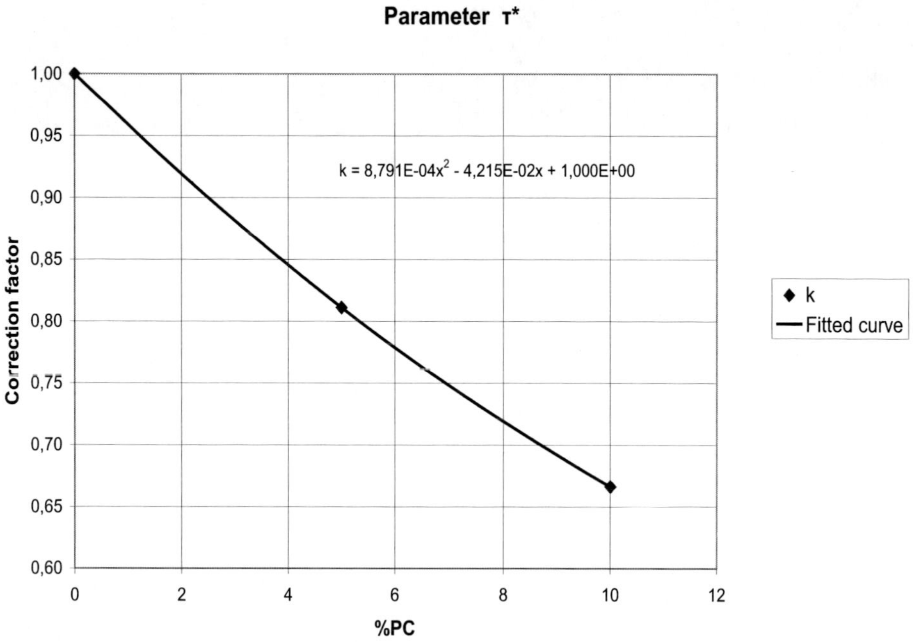

Figure 9. Correction factor graph of the τ^* parameter in relation to the PC content.

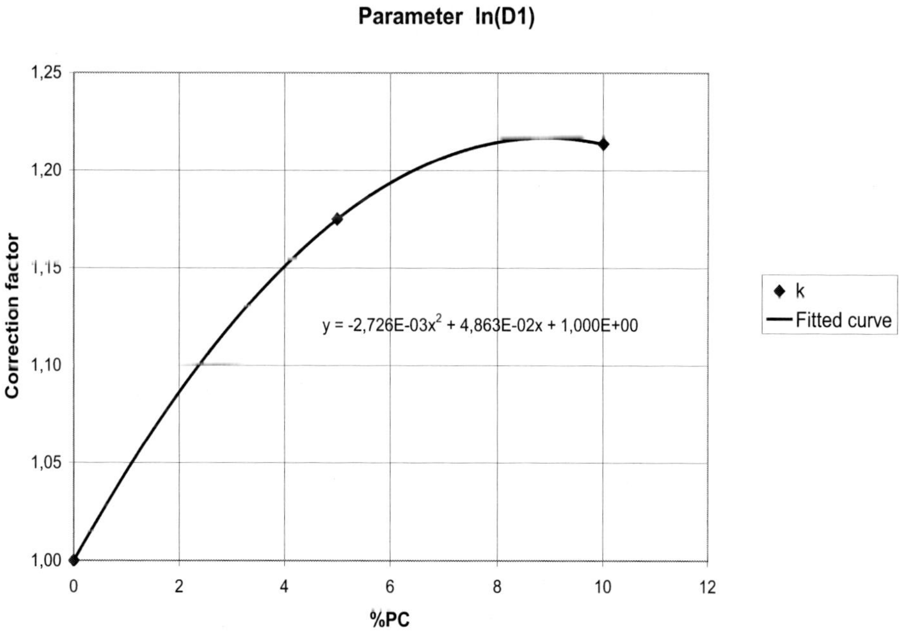

Figure 10. Correction factor graph of the ln(D_1) parameter in relation to the PC content

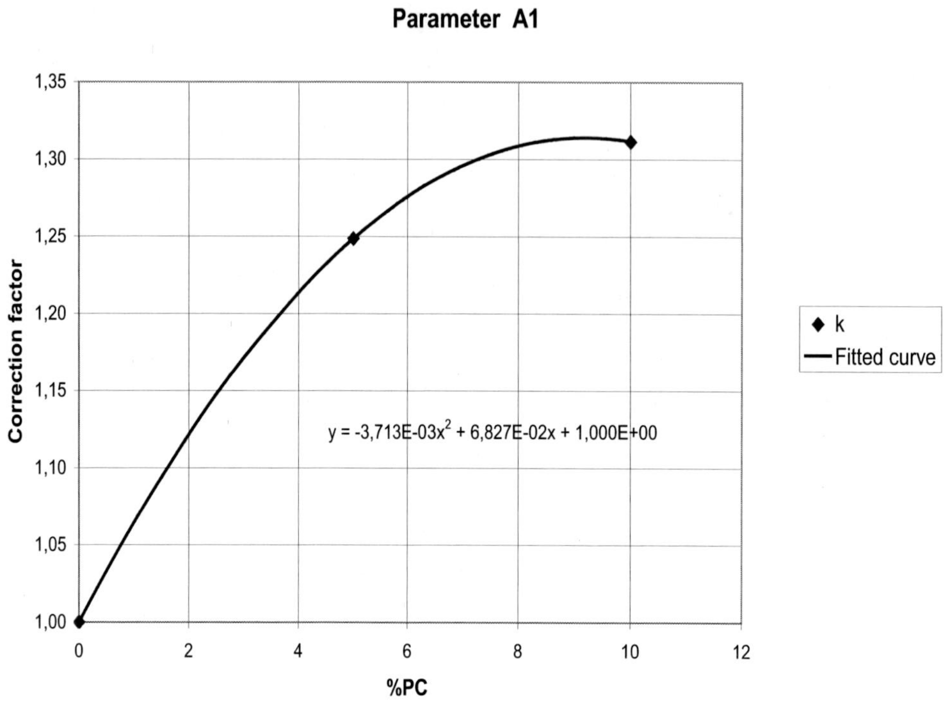

Figure 11. Correction factor graph of the A1 parameter in relation to the PC content

By means of approximations to a second-order polynomial by linear regression, the expressions of the different proportionality factors are obtained for each parameter with regard to the % of PC existing in the blend. These expressions are as follows:

$$
\begin{aligned}
k_n &= -2,279 \cdot 10^{-5} \cdot x_{PC}^2 + 2,534 \cdot 10^{-2} \cdot x_{PC} + 1 \\
k_\tau &= 8,791 \cdot 10^{-4} \cdot x_{PC}^2 - 4,215 \cdot 10^{-2} \cdot x_{PC} + 1 \\
k_{\ln(D_1)} &= -2,726 \cdot 10^{-3} \cdot x_{PC}^2 + 4,863 \cdot 10^{-2} \cdot x_{PC} + 1 \\
k_{A_1} &= -3,713 \cdot 10^{-3} \cdot x_{PC}^2 + 6,827 \cdot 10^{-2} \cdot x_{PC} + 1
\end{aligned}
\qquad (9)
$$

where:

x_{PC} [%] is the PC proportion in the blend.

k_i [-] is the correlation factor of the *i* parameter.

These factors are proposed to correct the variable parameters of the models corresponding to the three MFI intervals with regard to the PC content in the recycled ABS/PC blend.

By applying these factors, the following parameters are found:

$$
\begin{aligned}
n_{x_{PC}} &= k_n \cdot n_{0\%} = \left(-2,279 \cdot 10^{-5} \cdot x_{PC}^2 + 2,534 \cdot 10^{-2} \cdot x_{PC} + 1\right) \cdot n_{0\%} \\
\tau^*_{x_{PC}} &= k_\tau \cdot \tau^*_{0\%} = \left(8,791 \cdot 10^{-4} \cdot x_{PC}^2 - 4,215 \cdot 10^{-2} \cdot x_{PC} + 1\right) \cdot \tau^*_{0\%} \\
D_{1_{x_{PC}}} &= D_{1_{0\%}}^{\ k_{\ln(D_1)}} = D_{1_{0\%}}^{\left(-2,726 \cdot 10^{-3} \cdot x_{PC}^2 + 4,863 \cdot 10^{-2} \cdot x_{PC} + 1\right)} \\
A_{1_{x_{PC}}} &= k_{A_1} \cdot A_{1_{0\%}} = \left(-3,713 \cdot 10^{-3} \cdot x_{PC}^2 + 6,827 \cdot 10^{-2} \cdot x_{PC} + 1\right) \cdot A_{1_{0\%}}
\end{aligned} \tag{10}
$$

CONCLUSIONS

If the behaviour model foreseen for the material, in accordance to the proposed model, is compared to the real behaviour (**Figure 12**) within the range corresponding to the typical shear velocity values of the injection-moulding, then the following conclusions can be obtained:

- The approximation means an overrate of the real material viscosity, which in the simulation will mean a greater jump in the injection pressure among the different cavity points, and a greater level of the material dissipation energy by internal friction.
- If the minimum viscosity values obtained for interval 3 are considered, the recycled material remains very close to these values, which was foreseeable, given that the maximum flows considered in this interval are values which are close to those measured for the 3 mixtures.
- The goodness-of-fit test between the observed values and those expected values shows that no dependence exists among them (probability values lower than $3,06018 \cdot 10^{-47}$), which means that the expected results, as was foreseen, cannot be considered as being representative of the analyzed material and of its different mixtures. This must not lead to the model being rejected due to the fact that it is assessed as an average behaviour of the different ranges which are grouped in the same MFI indices interval.

As a consequence of the aforementioned conclusions, the adoption in the first approximation of the behaviour foreseen by the model is considered as appropriate to be contemplated in the recycled material, and always with the view of being catalogued within the proposed MFI indices ranges.

On the other hand, the introduction of PC in the mixture causes the viscosity differentiation, being greater when the PC content is higher, which confirms that the material flow is higher with an increase of this content.

The consideration of the viscosity variation with regard to the PC content of the blend may be introduced by means of the Cross-WLF model parameter correction, calculated in the previous section, whose comparison with the real recycled material is shown in **Figure 13** and 14.

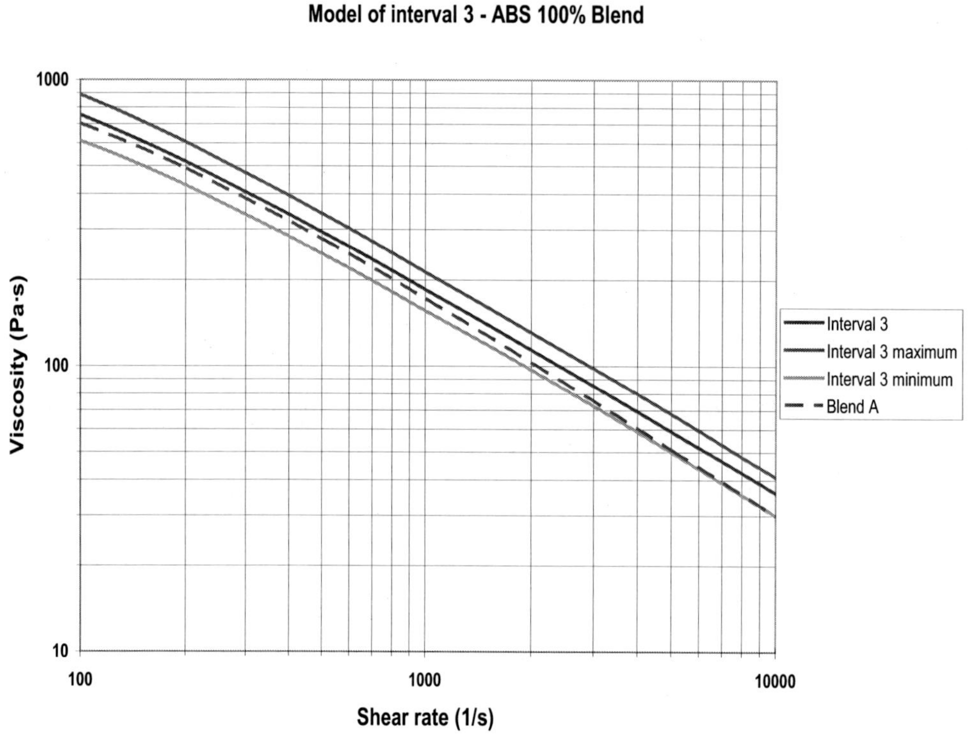

Figure 12. Viscosity graph of the blend A and model graph of the interval 3 behaviour (T = 220 ºC, p = 0 Pa).

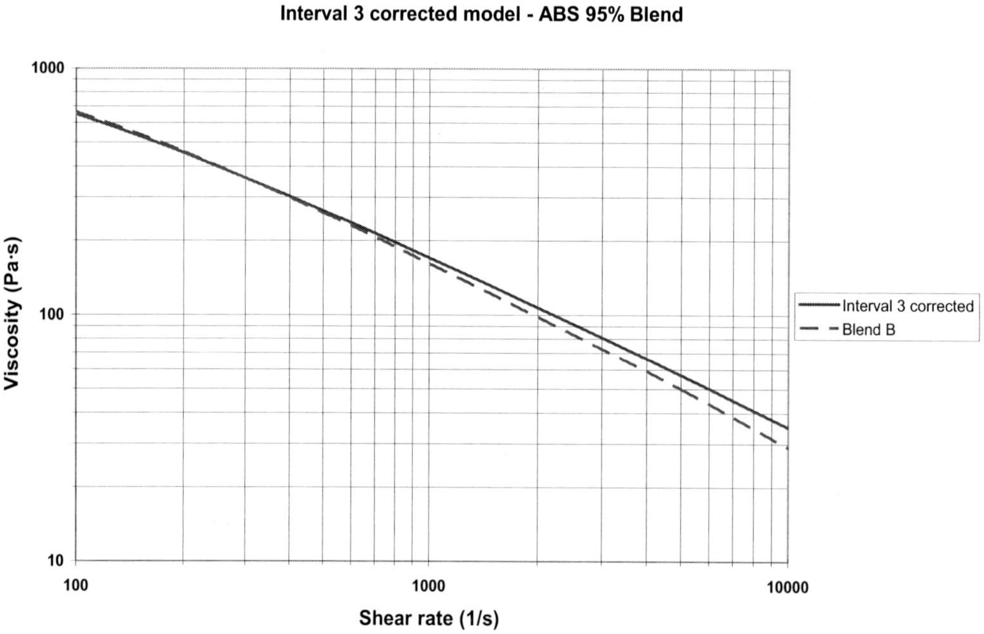

Figure 13. Viscosity graph of the blend B and the model graph of the interval 3 behaviour corrected with 5% PC (T = 220 ºC, p = 0 Pa).

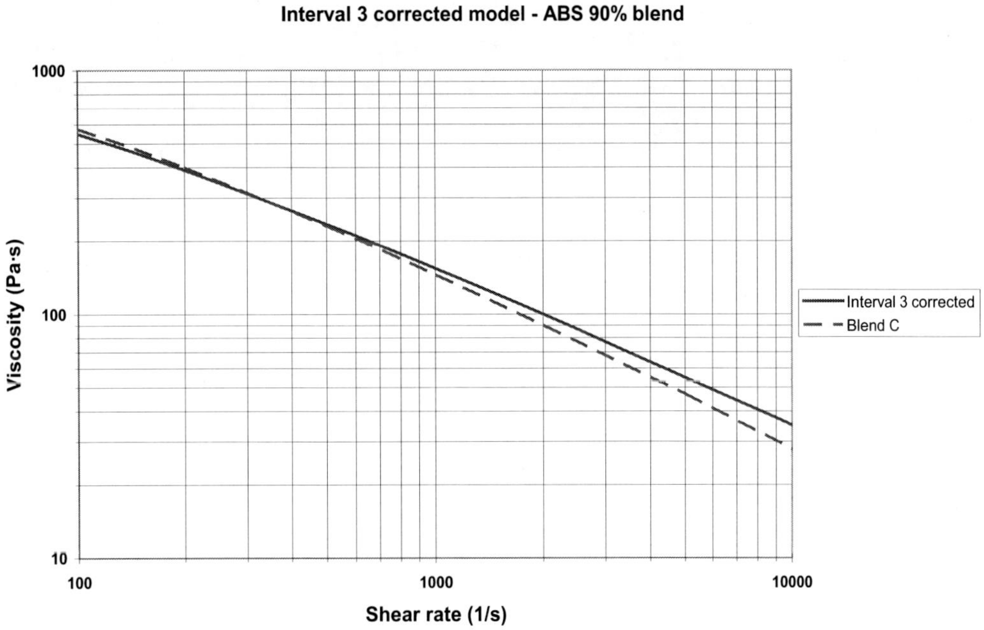

Figure 14. Viscosity graph of the blend C and the model graph of the interval 3 behaviour corrected with 10% PC (T = 220 ºC, p = 0 Pa).

As can be checked out, the adjustment of the viscosity with the proposed correction is valid when compared with the tested recycled material blends.

References

[1] Eguiazabal, J.I.; Nazabal, *J. Polymer engineering & science*, Vol. 30 (9), PP 527 – 531 (1990).

[2] Larsson, H.; Bertilsson, H. *Polymer recycling*, Vol. 1 (4), PP 243 – 248 (1995).

[3] Williams, M.L.; Landel, R.F.; Ferry, J.D. *Journal of the American Chemical Society*, Vol. 77, PP. 3701 – 3707 (1955).

[4] Poslinky, A.J. *Journal of Injection Molding Technology*, Vol. 1 (1), PP 57 – 71 (1997).

[5] Koster, R. *SPE ANTEC Technical Papers*, Vol. 48 (2002).

[6] Advanced CAE technology, Inc. "*C-Mold reference manual*". Advanced CAE Technology, Inc., 1997.

In: New Developments in Polymer Analysis, Stabilization... ISBN 1-59454-511-1
Editors: G.E. Zaikov and A. Jiménez, pp. 33-44

Chapter 3

Effect of Processing Variables on Environmental Stress Cracking Resistance in LDPE Injected Parts

S. Ferrándiz, J. Seguí and M. J. Reig
Universidad Politécnica de Valencia, Escuela Politécnica Superior de Alcoy,
Passeig del Viaducte nº1, Alcoy, Valencia, Spain.
e-mail:sferrand@mcm.upv.es; jsegui@mcm.upv.es; mjreig@mcm.upv.es
J. A. García
Universidad Politécnica de Valencia, Instituto de Diseño para la Fabricación, Camino de Vera s/n, 46022 Valencia, Spain. e-mail: jugarcia@mcm.upv.es

Abstract

The present work studies the environmental stress cracking (ESC) on LDPE pieces. In this paper we analyze the most recent prediction theories on the behavior of ESCR in LDPE pieces, and the relationships and effects between the variables of the injection process and the resulting behavior of the material.

Keywords: ESC, ESCR, LDPE, Stress cracking

Introduction

It is well known that plastic materials crack due to small internal stresses when the material is in contact with stress-crack agents. This phenomenon is known as Environmental Stress Cracking (ESC). The transformation of the material plays an important role in generating residual stresses, as a consequence of the thermal characteristics of the material. Arnold [14] explains that the most widely accepted approach is that the diffusion of stress-crack agent in the polymer causes hardening on the surface layer, increasing the capacity of chain movements. Such stresses generate gaps, which in turn act as preferable places for diffusion, causing the gaps or bubbles to join until forming cracks. It has been shown that to form cracks sufficient hardening must occur to produce stress/deformation or vice versa. This contradicts the concept of critical stress or critical deformation for each combination of polymer/stress-crack agent. The degree of hardening will depend on the amount of the diffusing stress-crack agent and on the size of the molecules of the stress-crack agent.

Raman, Farris and Lesser [15] give an excellent introduction presenting the different approaches that explain the phenomenon of Stress Cracking. The first approach mentioned by these authors is the diffusion of the agent in the polymer and the subsequent generation of induced stress caused by polymer swelling. This does not explain stress cracking in polymers caused by weak stress-crack agents, in which swelling practically does not occur. Therefore, the mechanism of swelling cannot be considered as the triggering element. Millar and Visser propose that solvent cracking occurs due to the stresses caused by the crystallization of the polymer induced by swelling. Since this approach does not explain appropriately most of the experiments, then crystallization by swelling cannot be considered as the mechanism of stress cracking. A different approach establishes that chain breaking causes mechanical and chemical degradation. Since the ESC problem involves physical interactions, not all systems experience degradation. The two most important ESC working hypotheses have been the reduction of the surface energy and hardening. The hypothesis of surface energy reduction causes the wetting of the surface of the gaps in the crack. Organic agents reduce the energy required for the formation of cracks.

The hypothesis of hardening establishes that the solvent and its vapors reduce the transition vitreous state and thus stress decreases near the crack front. Another author explains that these two hypotheses complement a third hypothesis. This third hypothesis is based on the evidence that hardening results from the fact that the relationship between the critical stress of the crack lacks the transition temperature drop due to solvent action. Kambour performed a study based on this hypothesis [1]. He observed through different experiments that solvents possess similar solubility parameters. On the other hand, Wright proposed the criterion of crack dissolution [5]. He said that the crack initiates when the inelastic stress reaches the critical value. All these theories do not take into account the effect of morphology and orientation. Gent explained that the polymer is exposed to a specific combination of expansion stresses and liquids and vapors that can wet an unstable formation. Based on the Flory-Huggins theory, which studies the behavior of swelling in entangled rubber, the author extends this behavior -a function of the molar fraction, expansion stress and the parameter of polymer-solvent interaction- to some points of surface concentration at which the swelling effects due to local expansion stresses are located. These authors finished their work explaining that PC films, for multiaxial stresses, show that well oriented polymers break at lower stresses than ill-oriented polymers.

Lagarón established that failure acceleration in the samples used is due to the absorption of the stress-crack agent by the polymer, causing the lubrication of the polymer chains, and thus early failure under conditions of small load growth. This effect is supported by the reduction in the activation energy. Other authors think that this absorption occurs in the amorphous phase.

Lagarón's research was based on the detection of the stress-crack agent in the amorphous phase by SEM complemented with IR tests. He said that only IR permits to observe the stress-crack agent in the amorphous phase of the polymer. He concluded by saying that he had intended to show the presence of the stress-crack agent in the polymer using the IR technique. The stress-crack agent is present along the transition fronts of the material, where the most effective stresses act and where the changes in the material occur. However, he suggested a stress mechanism induced by the diffusion of the stress-crack agent through the polymer chains. The diffusion of the molecules of the detergent due to stresses increases the mobility of the polymeric chains reducing their activation energy, thus causing the effect of hardening. It is understood that the stress-crack agent plays an important role in the process of induced elongation. Bubbles and subsequent fibrilation were observed in the presence of the stress-crack agent.

Al-Zubi based his analysis on PE transformed by rotational molding [25]. His work is very interesting as it is the most recent approach on ESC behavior. It presents the definition of failure by stress cracking as microcracks or surface fractures caused by the combination of stresses and environmental effects (fracturing agent). This author explains that polyethylene morphology is the main factor in the environmental stress cracking resistance of the material (ESCR). Polyethylene is divided in crystalline regions and amorphous regions which impregnate the crystalline regions forming continuous matrices. However, there is a third region that is very important and critical in the behavior of the material against ESCR. This region is the limit or interface between the crystalline region and the adjacent amorphous region. Exploring this last zone it can be seen that there is a certain level of arrangement in the molecular chains. This zone experiences greater load stresses and actually transfers the loads and reactions to the crystalline chains.

In this array, there are molecular chains that can start in the crystalline phase and end in the amorphous phase, can extend in the amorphous phase and return to the crystalline zone, or even can pass through all the amorphous phases to end up in a new crystalline phase. It is believed that this last configuration gives polyethylene its resistance to stress cracking. This structure is called tie molecules and act as coating between adjacent crystalline regions.

In order to understand ESC, it is necessary to examine what happens. Intuitively, it was believed that stress cracking started by the breaking of the molecules. This microscopic fracture propagated until forming a larger crack. This process was called degradation. Degradation increases crystallization in detriment of the amorphous region. This phenomenon is known as chemo-crystallization. However, it is more reasonable to think that this phenomenon occurs in the limits of the amorphous region and not in the middle of the region, due to the disorder and entanglement of the polymeric chains.

Great amounts of energy are required to create new crystalline zones, and thus polyethylene must be in the molten state to form them. Once cooled down, the crystalline zones contain low energy since they have a stable structure. The disordered amorphous zone is not as stable as the crystalline zone, but it is free of stresses since the molecules can move freely. Therefore, it is in the limit between these two states where all the processes of stress generation occur. It can be concluded that this limit zone is thermodynamically stressed and hence more inclined to stress cracking. These two zones (amorphous and crystalline) cool at different rates, corroborating the issues mentioned above. The energy required to allow the molecule to break or degrade in this zone can be reached with stresses such as those caused by warping or by the action of stress-crack agents.

EXPERIMENTAL

Due to the increasing number of testing methods, it is necessary to adopt a strategy that allows to evaluate stress cracking in plastics. Maxwell [28] presented a practical guide for test evaluation based on the nature of the results to obtain (Table 1).

Table 1. Test Evaluation Guide

Test type	Result	Testing time
Constant Deformation	Fractures/ does not fracture	Variable
Constant load	Starts deformation	Variable
Low deformation rate	V, K,	Few hours
Cracking mechanism	V,K	Variable
Fatigue	V, K	Frequency function

The most common and simple method follows ASTM 1693 standard, also called Bell Telephone. Using notched specimens, the sample is bent and mounted on a profile. Then, the profile is placed in a tube with the stress-crack agent and immersed in a mild bath. The readings are expressed in cracking percentage. This test is suitable for the comparison of behavior and/or processing. This test is widely used for quality control. The critical comments [29] come from the fact that variations in the specimen stiffness can give contradictory results. These experiments are considered as tests at constant stresses for 3 pt and 4 pt bent strip tests [28].

The tests performed in our work followed the Bell Telephone model, as indicated in ASTM- D 1693 standard. The stress-crack agent used was Arkopal, a stress-crack agent similar to Igepal C-630, with a polyglicolic ether of nonilphenol with 9 molecules of ethylene oxide. The specimens were 2 mm thick, and 30 x 13 mm in size, with a notch in the middle 0.3 mm thick. The first tests were performed at 10%, 20% and 45 % packing pressures. We also took into account the orientation of the input flow in the specimens. The parallel flow is expressed as in Figure 1.

The dark line indicates the origin of the specimen and the zone of the strip analyzed. Perpendicular flow (figure 1), refers to the zone shown in the following figure, in which the arrangement of the fibers is perpendicular to the position of the sampling strip in the test.

RESULTS AND DISCUSSION

Kambour [1] establishes the following relationships:

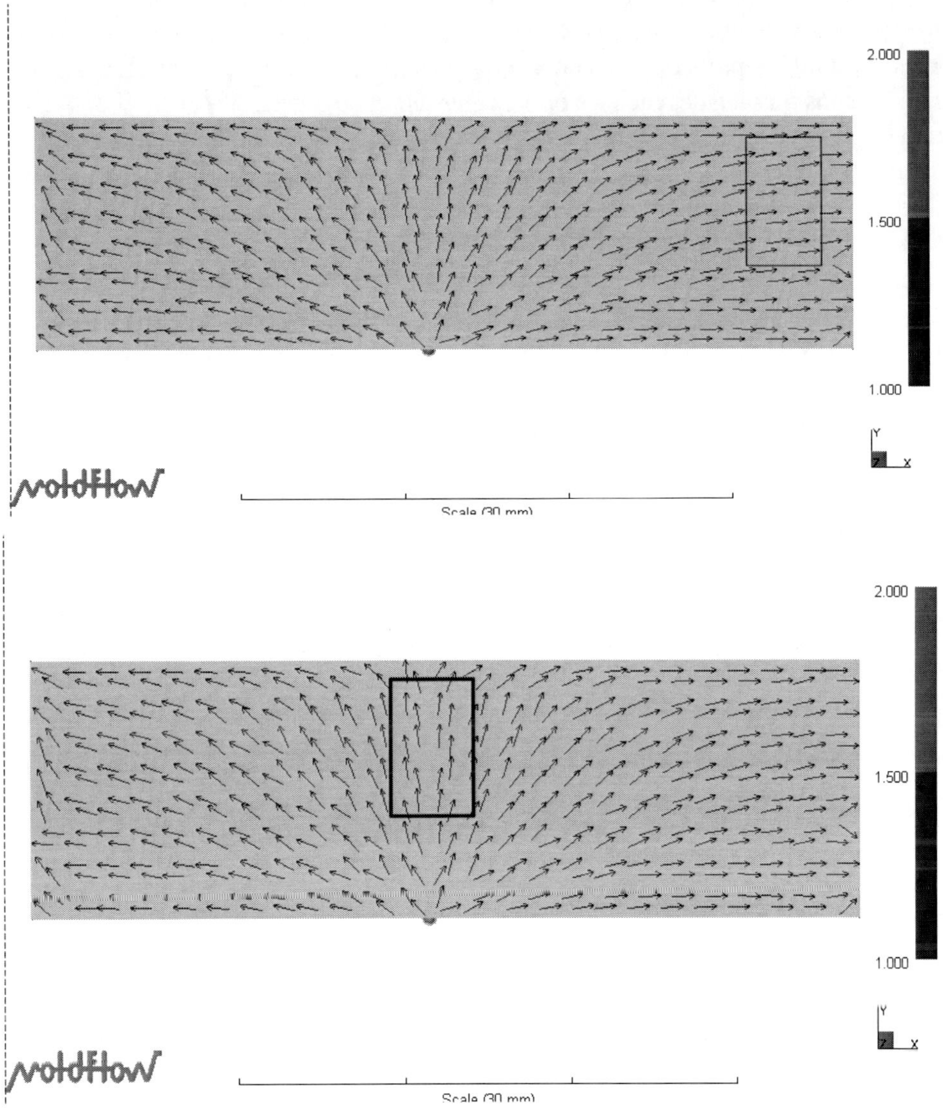

Figure 1. Representation of parallel and perpendicular flow and specimen situation

- Nucleus pressurization during solidification produces high density. When the mold is opened, the nucleus tries to recover its normal density in a short time.
- Differential aging between nucleus and surface. Densification rates initially depend on initial density, which depends on the pressure at which it is subjected during cooling. As a consequence, by cooling first the surface than the nucleus, internal stresses appear in the material that can accumulate on the surface by aging.
- Many greater degrees of stresses can be obtained by excessive mold packing. This is called overpacking. At small thicknesses, the polymer is oriented normal to the machine shaft. Therefore, there is a clear sensitivity to compacting pressures.

In the experimental tests spontaneous cracks appeared on the surface caused by the high working pressures. These areas correspond to 0.15 and 0.08% of the total area.

The orientation shows a beneficial effect on environmental stress cracking resistance. At the sprues, with higher pressure, the cracks propagate in the direction of the longest zone of the sprue. There is a strong dependence of the compacting pressures.

Strebel [26] established the relation of variables in blow molding, relating melting temperatures, mold temperatures and cycle times. The conclusions reached in his study are that by decreasing mold temperatures from 15°C to 3°C, failure time increases in about 11 hrs, due to the formation of tie molecules, which increases stress-crack resistance. A greater nozzle temperature causes premature degradation, which results in a lower resistance to stress cracking.

The results obtained are shown in Figures 2-4:

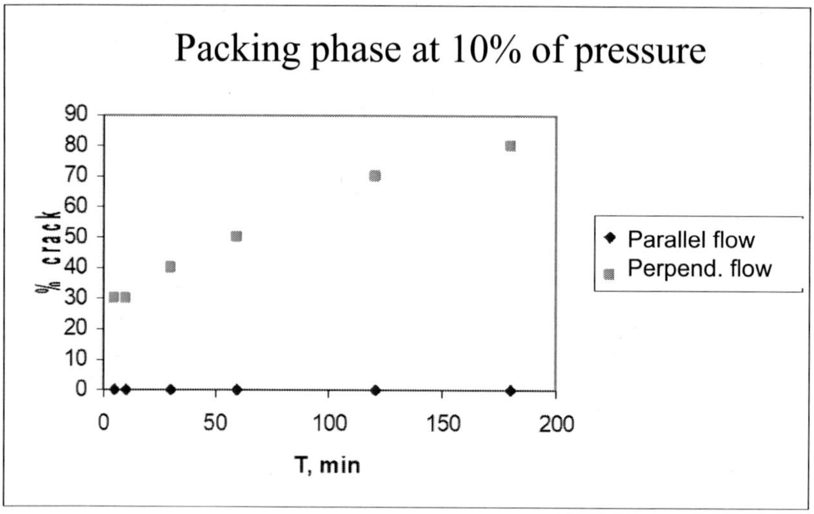

Figure 2. Results of packing phase at 10 % of pressure.

It can be observed that the presence of cracks or environmental stress cracking resistance (ESCR), is much lower for the specimens with flow perpendicular to the direction of the testing stress. This fact can also be observed at 20 and 45% of packing pressures, figures 3 and 4.

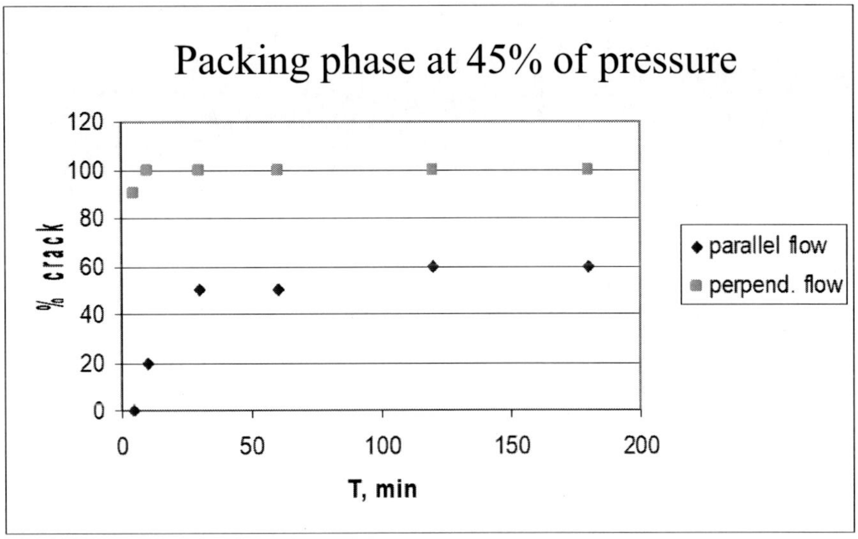

Figure 3. Results of packing phase at 45% of pressure

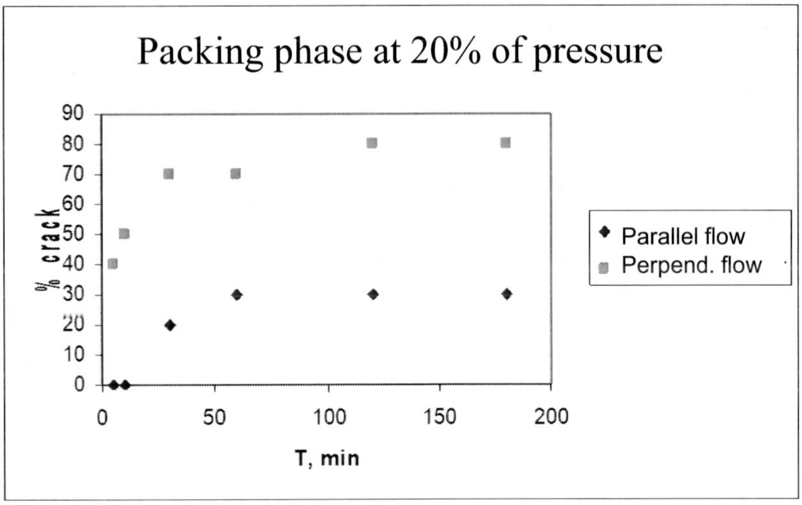

Figure 4. Results of packing phase at 20% of pressure

Comparing the same orientations in the three diagrams it can be observed that greater packing pressure affects stress cracking resistance. As a result, as the material is strongly compacted it needs more cooling time, which causes greater residual stresses and consequently longer cooling time. This can be observed in the diagram that shows DSC results, (figure 5) with different types of PE [30]

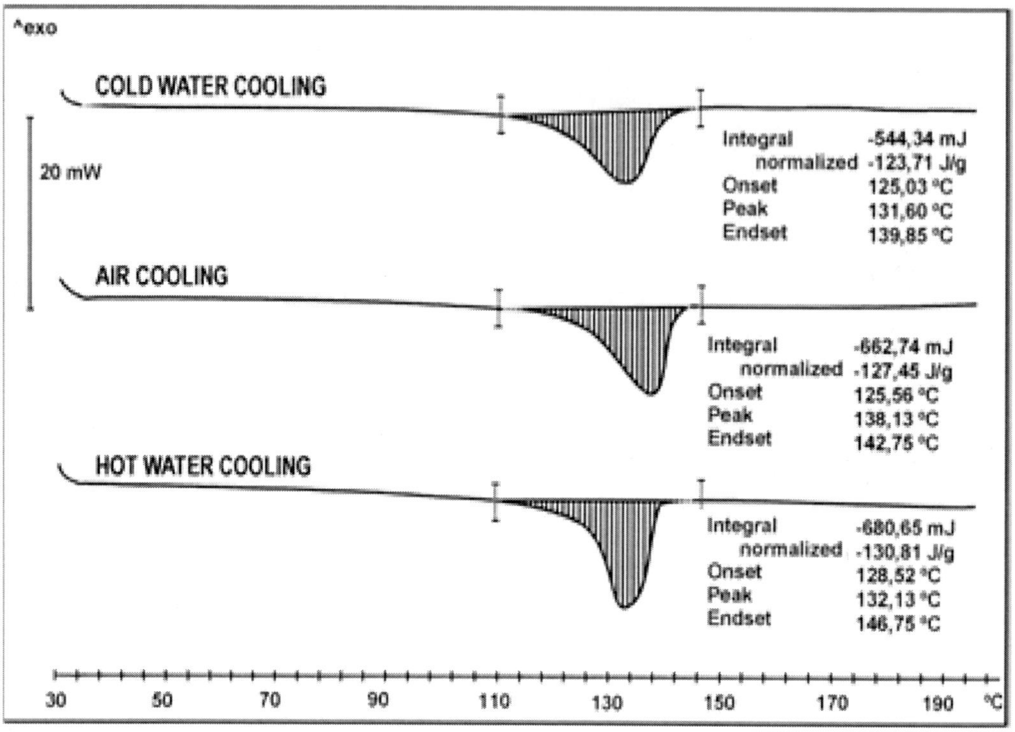

Figure 5. DSC results of cooling influence.

The following diagrams (Figures 6-8) show the residual stresses simulated under the conditions mentioned above, and the deformations that appear in the material

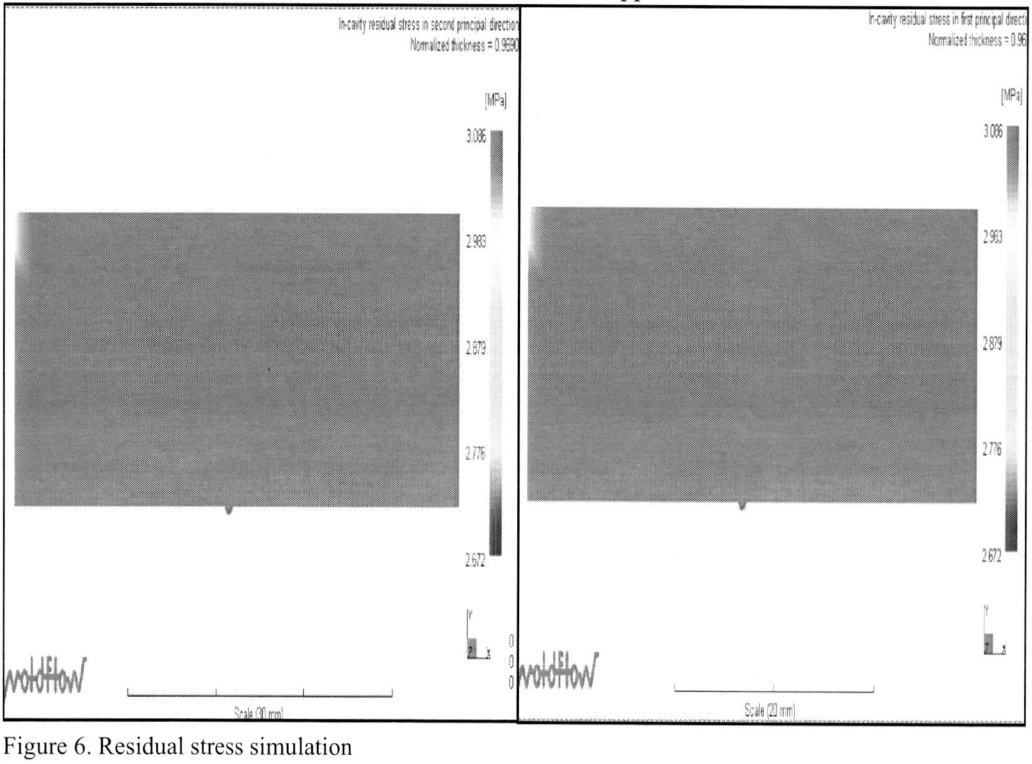

Figure 6. Residual stress simulation

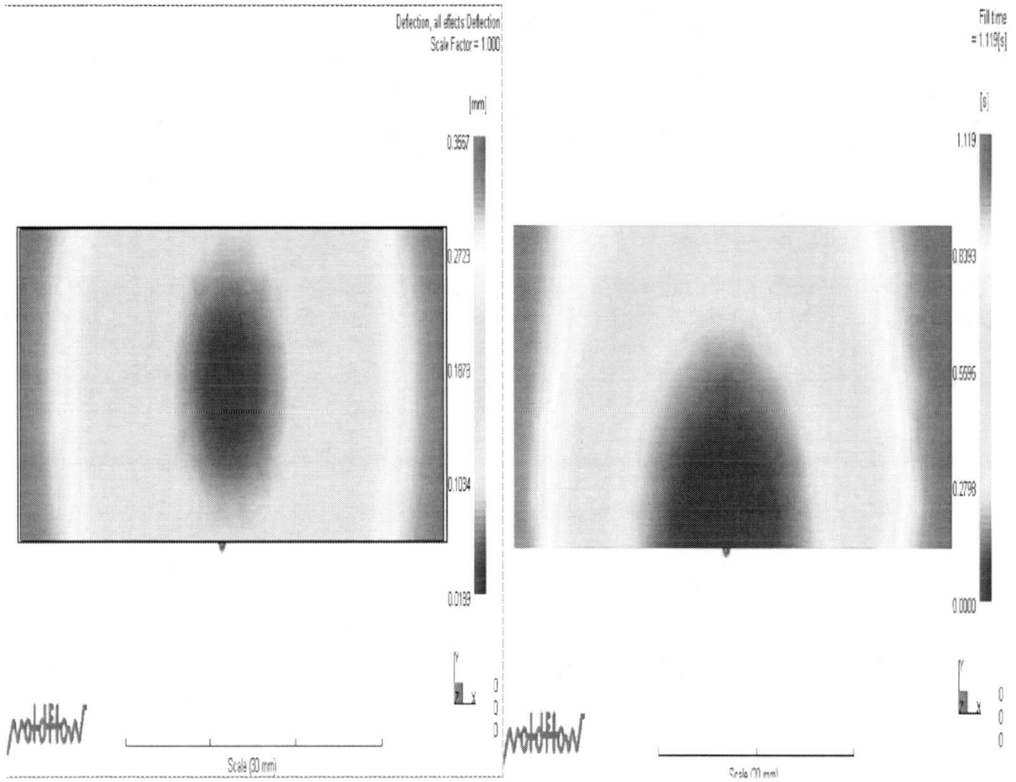

Figure 7. Deflection simulation

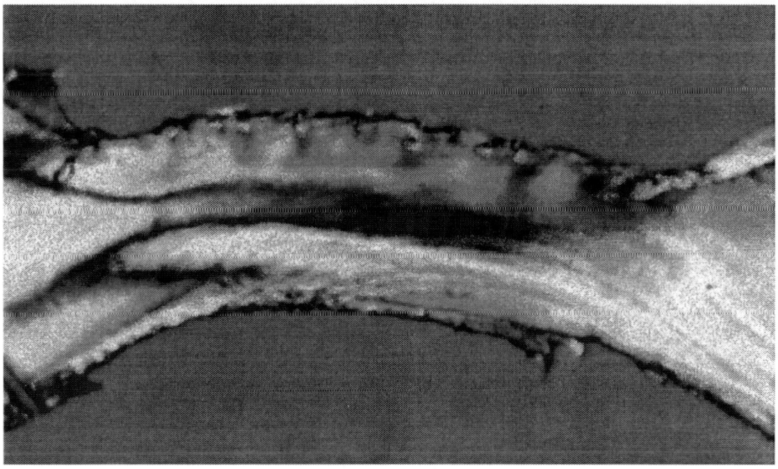

Figure 8. Residual stress microscopy

More data of the effects of the cooling rates on LDPE can be observed, as shown in Figure 9:

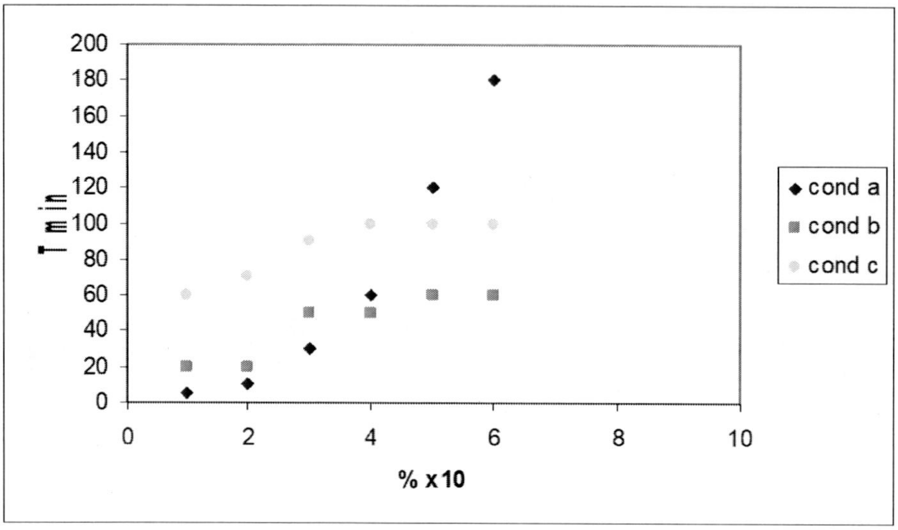

Figure 9. Processing conditions results

Under the conditions referred to as *a* (Figure 9) no cooling has taken place inside the mold. Under conditions *b* it took only 7 seconds of cooling time, and under conditions *c* it took 60 seconds. A greater resistance is observed in the non-refrigerated specimens cooled at room temperature. Finally, the graphs show three additional parameters: injection time, cooling time and compacting time, figure 10.

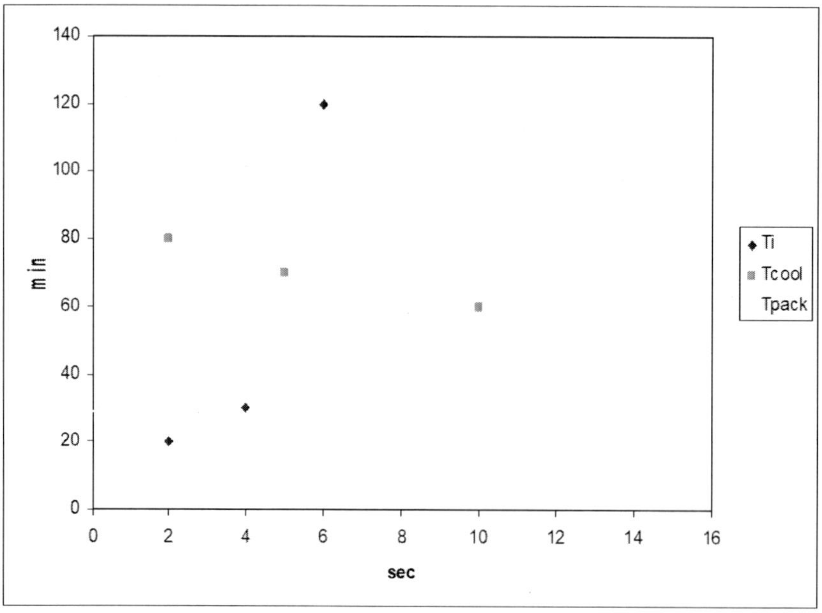

Figure 10. Times of injection, cooling and packing evolution

Better results are observed for long injection times, 6 seconds, (Figure 10). For short cooling times, stress cracking resistance improves, and for long compacting times, stress cracking resistance also improves.

CONCLUSIONS

Hellerich, Harsch, Haenle [31] stated that a well-transformed material presents no cracks due to environmental stress cracking. Therefore, stress cracking becomes a good method to assess the transformation quality of the material. We can say that if there is no good transformation in the material, at least it will be necessary to approach the stress cracking resistance values of the raw material. Thus, we can conclude that there are some parameters that affect environmental stress cracking resistance (ESCR) that can be inherent to the material itself. These characteristics are:

- Tie molecule density
- Molecular weight
- Solubility parameter (dispersion component, polar component and hydrogen link component)
- Crystallization (it depends on transformation)
- Orientation (it depends on transformation)

With respect to transformation, the parameters used have been injection times, specimen orientation relative to flow, compacting pressure, compacting time and cooling rate. Cracking, or rather environmental stress cracking resistance (ESCR), is lower for specimens in which the flow is perpendicular to the direction of the testing tensile direction Higher resistance is observed in non-refrigerated specimens cooled at room temperature. Better results were observed for long injection times, 6 seconds. For short cooling times, environmental stress cracking resistance improves; and for long packing times environmental stress cracking resistance also improves.

ACKNOWLEDGEMENTS

We would like to thank the Foreign Language Coordination Office at the Polytechnic University of Valencia for their help in translating this paper.

REFERENCES

[1] Kambour, Caraher, Schnoor, Todt, *Pol. Eng. Sci.* 1996, vol. 36(23).

[2] Soni, Geil, *J. Appl. Polym. Sci.vol* 23(4), 1979.

[3] Singlenton, Roche, Gail, *J. Appl. Polym. Sci.* vol 21,(9),1977.

[4] Hansen, I&EC *Prod. Res. Dev.* Vol.8 (1), 1969.
[5] Wright, D.C., 1996 William Andrew ed. ISBN 185957064X.
[6] Lagaron, Dixon, Reed, Pastor, Kip, *Polymer*, Vol. 40, 1999.
[7] Lagaron, Pastor, Kip, *Polymer* Vol 40, 1999.
[8] Turnbull, Maxwell, Pillai, *Polym. Testing*, vol 19, 2000.
[9] Maxwell, Turnbull, *NPL document,* 2003.
[10] Maxwell, Turnbull, *NPL report CMMT(A)* 288, 2000.
[11] Maxwell, MPL *report MATC(A)* 05, 2001.
[12] "Assessing ESC of amorphous thermoplastics*",* *www.esc-plastics.com* , 2003.
[13] "A predictive model for ESC: Solubility parameter, Size and shape*", www.esc-plastics.com* , 2003.
[14] Arnold, Taylor, *J. Polym. Sci.* vol 71, 1999.
[15] Raman, Farris, Lesser, *J. Appl. Polym.Sci*, vol 88, 2003.
[16] Kawaguchi, Nishimura, *Polym. Eng. Sci*, vol 43, (2), 2003.
[17] Qin, et al, *Antec papers* 1999.
[18] Soares, Aboot, Kim, *J. Polym .Sci.* vol 38, 2000.
[19] Dreze, Solvay polyolefins papers, 2003 .
[20] Marzinski, Lustiger, ANTEC papers, 2001.
[21] O'Connell, Duckett, Ward, *Polym. Eng. Sci*, vol 42, (7), 2002.
[22] Lesser, Paper PO049, 73rd Annual Meeting Soc. Rheol. 2001.
[23] Hsuan, Geotex. *Geomem,* vol 18, 2000.
[24] Hansen, Polym. *Degrad. & Stabil.* Vol 77, 2003.
[25] Al-Zubi, Brent Strong, Lampson web document, Poly Processing Company, 2002.
[26] Strebel, Benkson, *Polym. Eng. Sci*, vol 36, 1996.
[27] NPL, ESC Database Application, *www.npl.com.* 2003.
[28] Maxwell, Turnbull. NPL Report, CMMT(A)288, 2000. ISSN 1361-406.
[29] Brostow, Corneliusen, Lustiger, *Failure of plastics*, Hanser Ed. IBSN 0195207297.
[30] Balart, López, Sánchez, Nadal, "*Introducción a la ciencia e ingeniería de polímeros*", ISBN 84-607-3317-3, 2001.
[31] Hellerich, Harsch, Haenle. "Guía *de materiales plásticos: propiedades, ensayos, parámetros.*" Ed. Hanser. ISBN 8487454011.

In: New Developments in Polymer Analysis, Stabilization... ISBN 1-59454-511-1
Editors: G.E. Zaikov and Jiménez, pp. 45-55

Chapter 4

TOWARDS NANOSTRUCTURED MATERIALS BY MODIFICATION OF THERMOSETTING MATRICES WITH BLOCK COPOLYMERS

E. Serrano, M. Larrañaga, G. Kortaberria, P. M. Remiro and I. Mondragon*

Materials + Technologies` Group. Escuela Univ. Politekniko Unib. Eskola. Dpto. Ingeniería Química y M. Ambiente. Universidad País Vasco / Euskal Herriko Unibertsitatea. Pza. Europa 1, 20018 Donostia-San Sebastián, Spain

D. Mecerreyes

Centre for Electrochemical Technologies (CIDETEC), Parque Tecnológico de Miramón, Pº Miramón 196, 20009 Donostia-San Sebastián, Spain

ABSTRACT

Morphological behaviour of different block copolymers in thermosetting epoxy systems has been analysed in order to investigate their ability to generate nanostructured thermosetting systems. PEO-PPO-PEO block copolymers of low molecular weights and different molar ratios between blocks have been used to study the effect of curing temperature and copolymer composition on the morphology of thermosetting epoxy systems. Atomic Force Microscopy (AFM) analysis reveals that, for low molecular weights, the ability to generate nanostructured systems increases with PEO content as curing temperature diminishes. On the other hand, previously synthesized 64 % epoxidized SBS block copolymer has been used to evaluate epoxidation procedure used as a via to generate nanostructured thermosetting materials.

Keywords: Block copolymers, epoxy, nanostructured materials, self-assembling.

* Corresponding author. Tel.: +34-943017271; fax: +34-943017140. E-mail: iapmoegi@sc.ehu.es.

INTRODUCTION

Block copolymers are a fascinating class of polymeric materials made by the covalent bonding of two or more polymeric chains that, in most cases, are thermodynamically incompatible. These block copolymers are interesting for making nanostructured materials because of their tendency to self-assemble into a variety of equilibrium ordered phases, such as lamellae, cylinders and spheres [1-3].

The appearance of a particular equilibrium microstructure depends mainly on the chemical composition of the block constituents, their volume fractions and their architecture. Transitions between different morphologies (order-order and order-disorder transitions) are observed when varying composition and temperature [1-2]. For diblock copolymers in non-selective good solvents, these transitions can also be driven by changes in the polymer solution concentration, besides by changes in temperature. Other non-equilibrium ordered phases, such the bicontinuous double diamond structure, have also been detected [4-6].

Recent advantages of these nanomaterials are related to applications ranging from thermoplastic elastomers and high-impact plastics to pressure-sensitive adhesives, foams... Moreover, block copolymers are strong candidates for potential application in advanced technologies, such as information storage, drug delivery and photonic crystals [7-9].

In this work, the self-assembling ability of amphiphilic block copolymers is used for generating nanostructured materials in a controlled way onto thermosetting epoxy matrices modified with block copolymers.

It has been reported [10-12] that increasing polarity of block copolymers increases miscibility between them and uncured epoxy resin. In this sense, epoxidized natural rubber has been used as a more miscible rubbery modifier [13,14]. Moreover, the miscibility of block copolymers with the uncured epoxy resin is crucial to obtain self-assembling even for the cured state [10,15,16]. Recently we reported the synthesis and characterization of several epoxidized SBS block copolymers [17]. We found that miscibility between epoxy resin and epoxidized block copolymers increases with epoxidation level allowing these copolymers the possibility to generate nanostructured materials. In this work the ability of a high epoxidized SBS block copolymer as template for nanostructured resins has been analysed.

On the other hand, poly(ethylene oxide)-poly((propylene oxide)-poly(ethylene oxide) (PEO-PPO-PEO) triblock copolymers also get an amphiphilic character, with lipophilic (PPO) and hydrophilic (PEO) blocks, that leads to their self-assembling behaviour. The effect of temperature and concentration of a PEO-PPO-PEO block copolymer in aqueous solutions on the formation of micelles has been studied [18]. In a previous paper [19] we reported the effect of PEO-PPO-PEO content in dynamic-mechanical and morphological behaviour of thermosetting epoxy systems for two different curing temperatures. In this work we present the effect of curing temperature and composition of two different PEO-PPO-PEO block copolymers on the morphological behaviour.

EXPERIMENTAL

Materials

Block Copolymers

Two different poly(ethylene oxide)-block-poly(propylene oxide) (PEO-PPO-PEO) triblock copolymers from Polysciences, with weight-average molecular weights of 2,900 and 3,400 g/mol, and molar ratio between PEO and PPO blocks of 0.8:1 and 0.33:1, respectively, were used. Throughout this paper, these copolymers are denoted BC1 and BC2, respectively. These copolymers have the following structure:

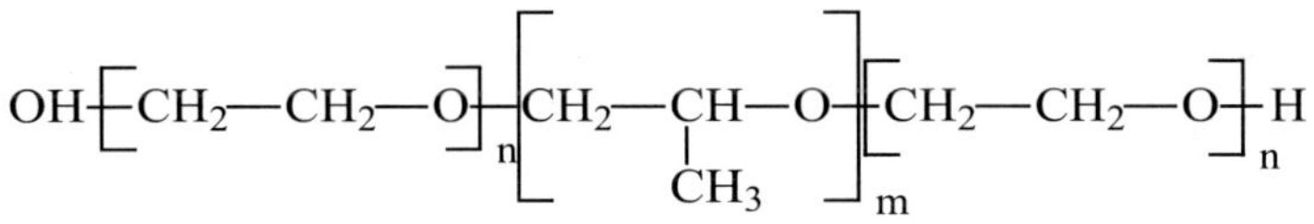

On the other hand, 64% epoxidized butadiene-block-styrene block copolymer, obtained by epoxidation of a commercial SBS star block copolymer, Kraton D-4272 CS (42.3 wt % polystyrene, 5.4 wt % 1,2-polybutadiene and 52.3 wt % 1,4-polybutadiene), was used. The details of its composition are described in a previous publication [17]. The epoxidation procedure used leads to mainly 1,4-epoxidized butadiene units. ^{1}H NMR peak integration values of signals attributed to cis- and trans- epoxy groups as compared to the remaining signals of the double bonds allowed calculating the degree of epoxidation of the copolymer. The structure of the epoxidized copolymers is:

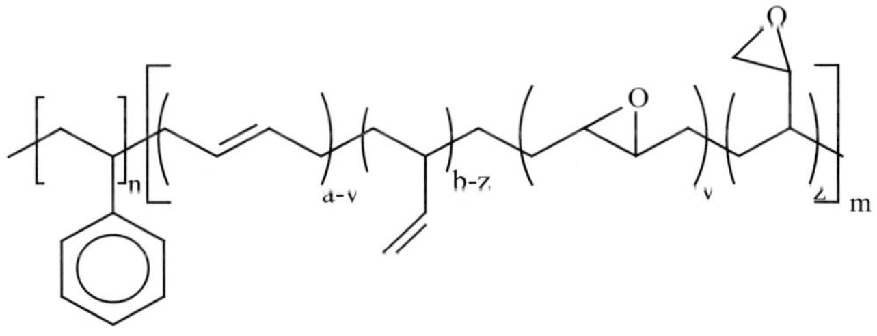

Thermoset Precursors

The epoxy monomer used, DER 332, was a diglycidyl ether of bisphenol-A (DGEBA), kindly supplied by Dow Chemical. It has an epoxy equivalent of around 175. The hardeners used were two aromatic diamines, 4,4′-diamino diphenyl methane (DDM) from Vantico and 4,4′-methylene bis(3-chloro 2,6-diethylaniline) (MCDEA) from Lonza. The epoxy monomer and the diamines were used in stoichiometric ratio.

Sample Preparation

PEO-PPO-PEO/epoxy cured samples were prepared by mixing the molten DGEBA with the block copolymer at 80 °C with continuous stirring. Afterwards, DDM was added to the mixture at the same temperature and stirred until a homogeneous ternary mixture was obtained. Then, the samples were degassed in vacuum and cured at 80, 100 and 120 ºC for 6 h, or at 140 ºC for 3 h. Finally, the samples were post-cured at 190 ºC for 2 h.

Epoxidized SBS/epoxy cured systems were prepared in the following way: firstly, the copolymer and the DGEBA were dissolved in THF. The resultant solution was heated at 80 ºC in an oil bath until complete solvent removal. Then the temperature was raised up to 110 or 140 ºC, and MCDEA was added to the sample. The samples were degassed at vacuum and cured at 110 ºC for 36 h or 140 ºC for 24 h.

Techniques

Atomic Force Microscopy (AFM)

The morphology of the specimens was studied by Atomic Force Microscopy *(AFM)*. A scanning probe microscope (Nanoscope IIIa, Multimode^{TM} from Digital Instruments) operating in *tapping mode (TM-AFM)* equipped with an integrated silicon tip / cantilever having a resonance frequency ~ 300 kHz from the same manufacturer was used. The height and phase images were obtained under ambient conditions with typical scan speeds of 0.5-1 line/s, using scan heads with a maximum range of 16 x 16 μm or 150 x 150 μm.

Rheology

Dynamic oscillatory shear measurements were performed using a Rheometrics Ares rheometer equipped with 25 mm diameter parallel plates and a transducer with a couple operating range of 0.02-200 g·cm. Samples of 13 mm diameter and 1.5 mm thickness were made by pressing the sample in a press with a force of 10 ton. After loading the sample in the rheometer, it was heated to 180 ºC for 10 min to erase all prior themomechanical history. Then the sample was cooled, always ensuring that the normal force was close to zero, so as not to induce any macroscopic alignment of the sample. The conditions of frequency and strain were carefully selected to ensure linear viscoelastic regime.

RESULTS AND DISCUSSION

PEO/PPO/PEO Triblock Copolymer / Epoxy Systems

Effect of Curing Temperature

The phase behaviour of thermosetting epoxy systems modified with linear block copolymers strongly depends on the curing conditions [20]. In this sense, DGEBA/DDM blends containing 20 wt % BC1 block copolymer were cured at different temperatures ranging from 80 to 140 ºC, and post-cured at 190 ºC. The influence of curing temperature on the morphological behaviour was investigated by TM-AFM (Figure 1). The cured blends are transparent at curing temperatures up to 120 ºC. They showed nanoscopic phase-separated morphology with domain sizes lower than 100 nm (Figures 1a-c). It has been reported that the block copolymer used is initially miscible with DGEBA/DDM system [19,21] but, on curing, PPO block phase segregates as the molecular weight of the epoxy system increases leading to self-assembly of PPO into spherical micelles. Moreover, the nanodomain size remains almost constant for curing temperatures of 80 and 100 ºC (Figures 1a and 1b). However, for blends cured at 120 ºC the size slightly increases (Figure 1c).

On the other hand, for 140 ºC cured blends the blends appear opaque thus indicating that microscopic phase separation takes place. As shown in Figure 1d, spherical microdomains with sizes ranging from 350 to 500 nm are formed. Thus, the ability of BC1 to generate nanostructured thermosetting materials depends on curing temperature. It has been reported that cloud point phase diagrams for PEO-PPO-PEO block copolymers present LCST (Lower Critical Solution Temperature) behaviour [20]. This means that cloud point conversion decreases as curing temperature increases. Then, it can be deduced that for 140 ºC curing temperature cloud point conversion for 20 wt % modified system is lower than gelification conversion. Subsequently, for 140 ºC curing temperature, microphase separation of BC1 takes place before gelification occurs.

Effect of Copolymer Composition

The effect of block copolymer composition on the morphological behaviour was studied by comparing BC2/DGEBA/DDM blends with the previously discussed ones containing BC1 block copolymer, which has higher PEO content.

DGEBA/DDM blends containing different BC2 contents have been cured at 80 and 140 ºC. Figure 2 shows TM-AFM images for different BC2-modified systems. All cured systems are microscopically phase separated into spherical domains. The blends are opaque thus confirming microphase separation.

The size of domains increases with curing temperature. For the 20 wt % modified system cured at 80 ºC (Figure 2b), the particles have a diameter of 0.7 μm. However, when curing temperature was 140 ºC, the particles have a bimodal size distribution with sizes ranging from 0.9 μm up to 1.8 μm (Figure 2c). Taking into account the LCST behaviour for these copolymers, cloud point conversions are lower at higher temperatures. As the viscosity of the system is lower for high temperatures, the mobility of particles increases and, as separated at lower cloud point conversion, they have the possibility to grow or coalesce before gelification takes place, leading to higher domain sizes.

By comparing these blends with the corresponding ones for BC1-modified epoxy systems, BC1 has the ability to generate nanostructured materials for curing temperatures lower than 140 ºC while the correspondent ones for BC2 block copolymer lead to microscopically phase-separated systems even for the 10 wt % BC2-modified system cured at 80 ºC. Block copolymers differ in molecular weight and molar ratio among blocks. Both have low and similar molecular weights, but PEO content increases from 20 wt % for BC2 up to 38 wt % for BC1. Thus, for low molecular weights, high PEO block contents increases the miscibility between DGEBA/DDM epoxy system and block copolymers, thus allowing them the possibility to generate nanostructured thermosetting materials.

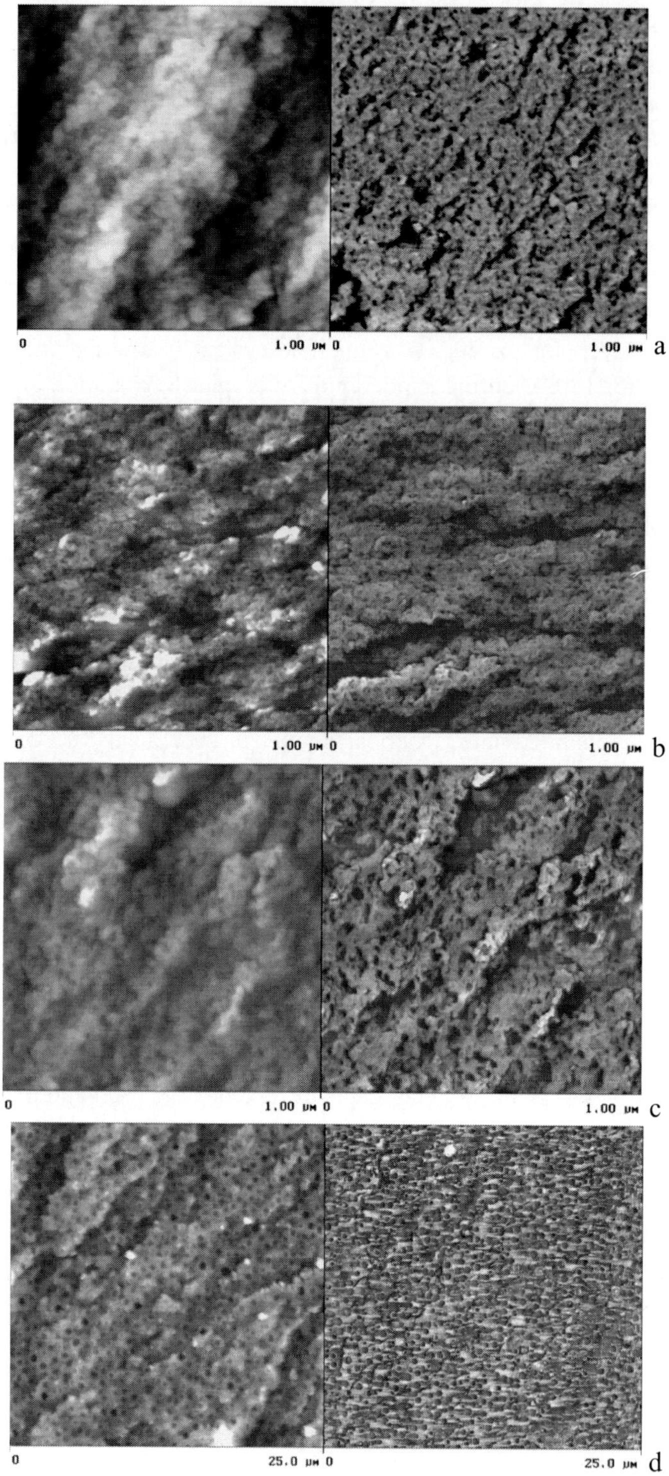

Figure 1. TM-AFM images of DGEBA/DDM blends containing 20 wt % BC1 cured at: (a) 80, (b) 100 and (c) 120 ºC for 6 h, and at (d) 140 ºC for 3 h, and all of them post-cured at 190 ºC for 2 h. Topographical (left) and phase (right) images.

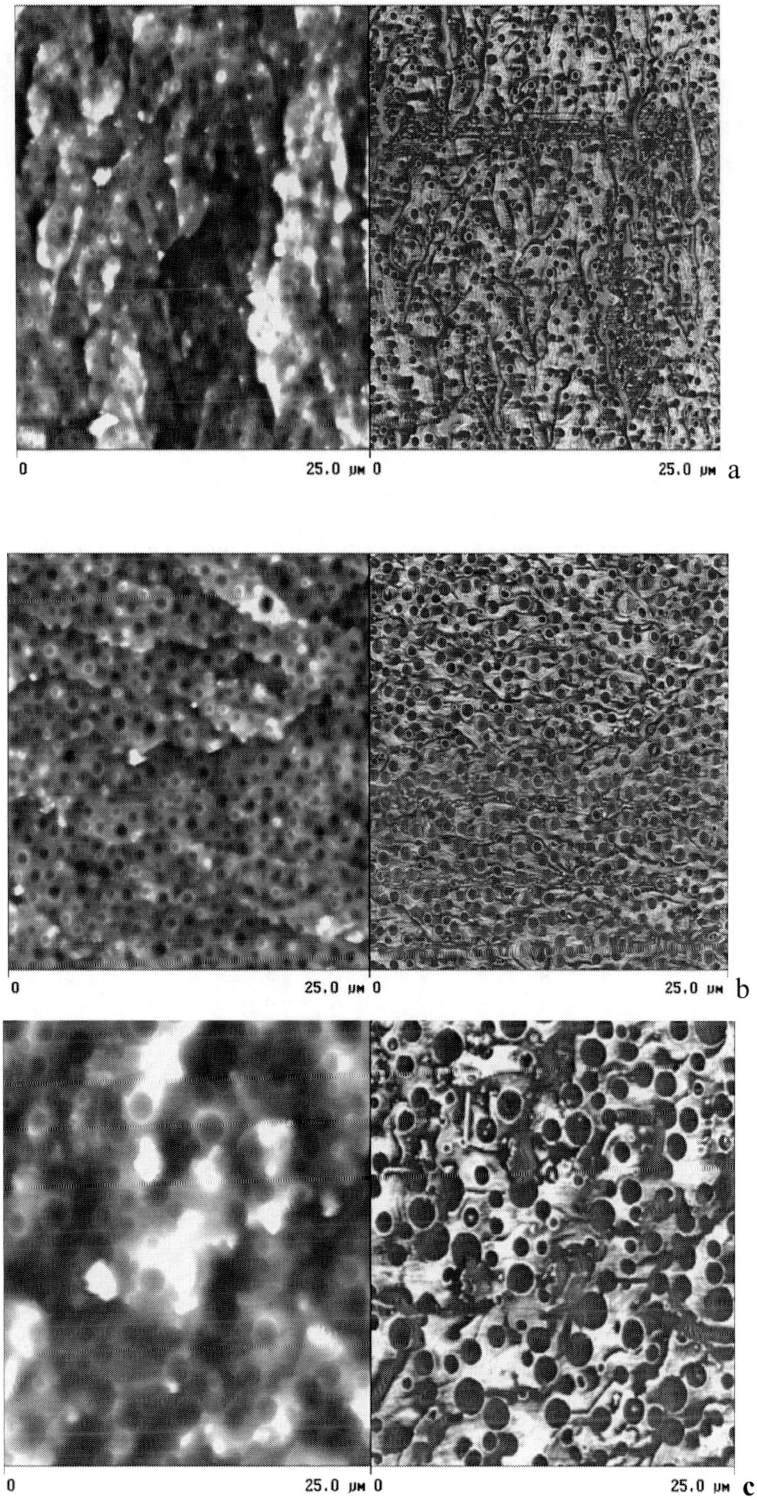

Figure 2. TM-AFM images of DGEBA/DDM blends containing different amounts of BC2: (a) 10 wt % and (b) 20 wt % cured at 80 ºC for 6 h, and (c) 20 wt % cured at 140 ºC for 3 h. All systems post-cured at 190 ºC for 2 h. Topographical (left) and phase (right) images.

Epoxidized SBS Block Copolymer/Epoxy Systems

Rheological measurements have been carried out in order to investigate the phase behaviour of 64% epoxidized SBS block copolymer. Figure 3 shows storage modulus (G′) and loss tangent (tan δ) dependence upon temperature for this copolymer.

The maximum peak of tan δ around 85 °C, which corresponds to the glass transition temperature (T_g) measured by DSC, can be attributed to T_g of polystyrene block. At higher temperatures, a gradual drop in the magnitude of G′ is observed between 115 °C and 125 °C, which can be attributed to a possible order-order transition temperature (T_{OOT}) for the neat block copolymer. By this reason, the curing temperatures chosen for curing SBS-modified systems were 110 °C and 140 °C, below and above T_{OOT}.

Figure 4 a-b shows self-assembling of DGEBA/MCDEA matrix containing 30 wt % of 64 % epoxidized SBS block copolymer cured at 110 and 140 °C, respectively. The corresponding blends for the epoxy matrix modified with the commercial SBS star block copolymer leads to a microscopically phase-separated system (not shown here). Both commercial and epoxidizidized SBS present UCST (Upper Critical Solution Temperature) behaviour. However, epoxidized block copolymer has higher miscibility window [17]. Thus, the epoxidation procedure used [17] leads to a block copolymer able to generate nanostructured thermosetting materials by improving miscibility between block copolymer and DGEBA.

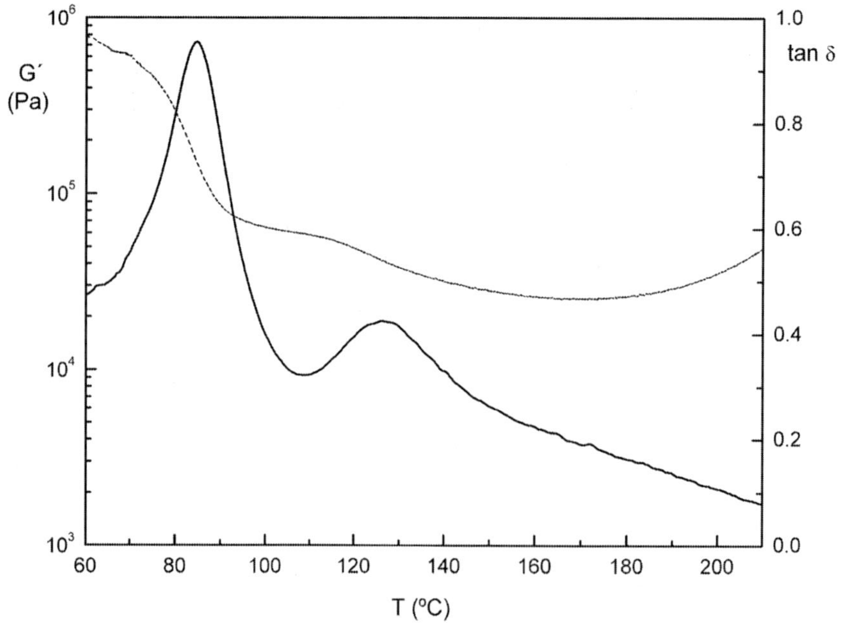

Figure 3. Isochronal temperature dependence of the storage modulus (---), G′, and loss tangent, tan δ, (—) for 64 % epoxidized SBS copolymer. The sample was previously heated to 180 °C for 10 min to erase all prior themomechanical history. Scan rate 2 °C/min.

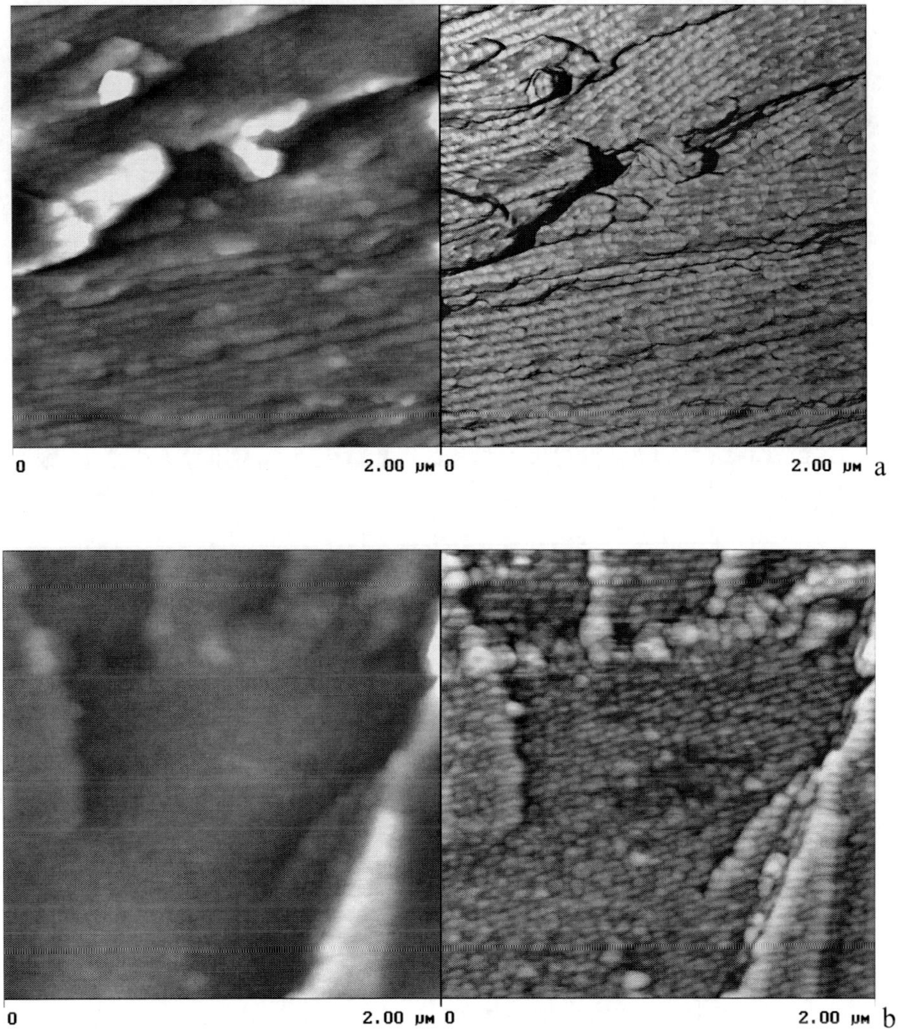

Figure 4. TM AFM images for DGEBA/MCDEA blends containing 30 wt % of 64 % epoxidized SBS copolymer cured at: (a) 110 ºC for 6 h and (b) 140 ºC for 24 h. Topographical (left) and phase (right) images.

On the other hand, AFM analysis seems to reveal the same morphology for both curing cycles. From rheological measurements previously showed different self-assembling behaviour should be expected. Nevertheless, phase behaviour of block copolymer can differ when it is blended with uncured epoxy resin. It has been reported [10] that miscible blends of block copolymer with uncured DGEBA self-assembled into a different morphology as block copolymer content changed. Then, the improved miscibility between epoxidized copolymer and epoxy resin would cause T_{OOT} displaced towards higher or lower temperatures. In future works a careful study of this system will be reported.

CONCLUSIONS

In this work, different aspects of the self-assembling behaviour of block copolymers into epoxy systems have been analysed. PEO-PPO-PEO block copolymers of low molecular weight and different molar ratio between blocks have been used to study the influence of both curing temperature and composition of the copolymer on the morphological behaviour of DGEBA/DDM epoxy systems. AFM images reveal that the ability to generate nanostructured thermosetting materials increases with PEO content and as curing temperature decreases as well. On the other hand, previously used epoxidation of the block copolymer [17] has been analysed as a procedure to obtain epoxidized SBS block copolymers able to generate nanostructured materials. AFM images reveal that DGEBA/MCDEA epoxy systems containing 30 wt % of 64% epoxidized SBS are able to generate nanostructures at temperatures higher than the T_g of polystyrene block. Future work will report phase behaviour of epoxy systems containing different percentages of several epoxidized block copolymers.

ACKNOWLEDGMENTS

The authors wish to express their gratitude to the Ministerio de Ciencia y Tecnología for funding this work (MAT2000-0293 and MAT2001-0714) and also to the Diputación Foral de Gipuzkoa for its financial support.

REFERENCES

[1] Leibler, L., *Macromolecules, 13:6* 1602-1617 (1980).
[2] Fredickson, G.H., Leibler, L., *Macromolecules, 22:3* 1238-1250 (1989).
[3] Bates, F.S., Fredickson, G.H., Phys. Today, *52:2* 32-38 (1999).
[4] Hadjichistidis, N., Pispas, S., Floudas, G.A., *Block copolymers Synthetic strategies, physical properties and applications.* Wiley Interscience. Hoboken (2003).
[5] Thomas, E.L., Alward, D.B., Kinning, D.J., Martin, D.C., Handling, D.L.Jr., Fetters, L.J., *Macromolecules, 19:8* 2197-2202 (1986).
[6] Likhtman, A.E., Semenov, A.N., *Macromolecules 27:11* 3103-3106 (1994).
[7] Hedrick, J.L., Miller, R.D., Hawker, C.J., Carter, K.R., Volksen, W., Yoon, D.Y., Trollsas, M., *Adv. Mater. 10:13* 1049-1053 (1998).
[8] Ahmed, S.B., Ogale, R.R., Kofinas, P., Papaefthymiou, G.C., *Appl. Phys. Lett., 80:9* 1616-1618 (2002).
[9] Hu, W., Gong, D., Chen, Z., Yuan, L., Saito, K., Grimes, C.A., Kichambare, P., *Appl. Phys. Lett., 79:19* 3083-3085 (2001).
[10] Grubbs, R.B., Dean, J.M., Broz, M.E., Bates, F.S., *Macromolecules, 33:26* 9522-9534 (2000).
[11] Remiro, P.M., Riccardi, C.C., Corcuera, M.A., Mondragon, I., *J. Appl. Polym. Sci., 74:4* 772-780 (1999).
[12] Chen, J.-L., Chang, F.-C., Macromolecules, *32:X* 5348-5356 (1999).
[13] Bussi, P., Ishida, H., *J. Appl. Polym. Sci., 53:4* 441-454 (1994).

[14] Cizravi, J.C., Subramaniam, K., *Polym. Int.*, *48:9* 889-895 (1999).
[15] Lipic, P. M., Bates, F. S., Hillmyer, M. A., *J. Am. Chem. Soc.*, *120:35* 8963-8970 (1998).
[16] Mijovic, J., Shen, M., Sy, J. W., Mondragon, I., *Macromolecules 33:14* 5235-5244 (2000).
[17] Serrano, E., Larrañaga, M., Remiro, P.M., Carrasco, P.M., Pomposo, J.A., Mecerreyes, D., Mondragón. I., *Macromol. Chem. and Phys.* (in press).
[18] Su, Y.-L., Wang, J., Liu, H.-Z., *Macromolecules*, *35:16* 6426-6431 (2002).
[19] Larrañaga, M., Gabilondo, N., Kortaberria, G., Serrano, E., Ricarddi, C.C., Mondragon, I., *Revista.* (in press)
[20] Guo, Q. *In Polymer Blends and Alloys.* Shonaike, G.O., Simon, G. Eds. Marcel Dekker. New York. Chapter 6, 155-187 (1999).
[21] Dean, J.M., Lipic, P.M., Grubbs, R.B., Cook, R.F., Bates, F.S., *J. Polym. Sci: Part B: Polym. Phys.*, *39:29* 2996-3010 (2001).

In: New Developments in Polymer Analysis, Stabilization... ISBN 1-59454-511-1
Editors: G.E. Zaikov and Jiménez, pp. 57-70

Chapter 5

CHARACTERIZATION OF THE BIODEGRADABLE POLYMER BIONOLLE [POLY(BUTYLENE SUCCINATE) - PBS]

J. Vega-Baudrit and M. Sibaja

Escuela de Química, POLIUNA, Universidad Nacional, 86-3000, Heredia, Costa Rica.

(Tel, Fax) (506) 277 3557 - (E-mail) jvegab@una.ac.cr

José Miguel Martín-Martínez

Adhesión and Adhesives Laboratory, Universty of Alicante, 03080 Alicante, Spain

K. Nakayama, T. Masuda and A. Cao

National Institute of Materials and Chemical Research. Higashi, Tsukuba, Ibaraki 3058565, Japan

ABSTRACT

Bionolle sheets -poly (butylene succinate) (PBS)- were prepared by extrusion. Biodegradability of PBS was associated to their molecular structure. In this study, crystallinity and morphology of PBS was modified by rolling stresses applied under uniaxial drawing. The variation of the PBS properties as a function of the draw conditions was studied. Changes in molecular structure and crystallinity were investigated by differential scanning calorimetry (DSC), dynamic mechanical thermal analysis (DMA), stress-strain tests, sonic modulus, X-ray diffraction, density and measurements of Haze percentage. The rolling improved the thermo-mechanical properties of the extruded PBS sheets as a result of changes in molecular orientation and crystallinity.

INTRODUCTION

The increased consumption of plastics generate important waste amount, which effects on the environment can no longer be neglected [1]. One technological alternative to reduce plastic wastes is the development of biodegradable polymers such as Bionolle (PBS) and other polymer blends [2-4,9,10]. These polymers can be degraded by microorganisms in soil and water, without polluting the environment.

This study addresses the improvement of the properties of biodegradable aliphatic polyester films by altering its molecular chain orientation. Some aliphatic polyesters (such as PBS) are biodegradable under microbial attack, so particular and unique applications can be developed. These materials have somewhat low melting point and lower mechanical properties as compared with aromatic polyesters [5]. For example, poly(hexane-6-lactone) - PCL- is an aliphatic polyester relatively stable under ambient conditions but it is biodegradable under microbial attack [6,10].

In this study, the morphology and molecular structure (whose are related to biodegradability) of an aliphatic polyester PBS was modified by applying rolling forces, and the modifications produced were examined.

EXPERIMENTAL

Materials

The synthesis and characterization of PBS has been already described in previous papers [6,7] and a patent [8]. This product was compared with commercial PBS – Bionelle 1000 (Showa Kobunshi LTD., Japan) which Mn is 55.200 and Mw = 113.000.

Sheet Processing

Sheets of PBS were obtained from pellets using a single-screw extruder (LABO PLASTOMILL, Toyoseiki Co) provided with a T-die (50 mm width and 0.6 mm clearance) at 60 rpm under screw rotation. Take-up speed was 2 m/min, and mass output was 49 g/min. The temperature of the chill roller was 50°C. The extrusion temperature profile in the barrel zones was set from hopper to die at 100, 135, and 140°C. PBS pellets were dried overnight in a vacuum oven at 80°C, and then, placed in a dry oven until use.

Uniaxial Stretching and Rolling

The polymer rolling mill machine, designed by Prof. Nakayama, consists in a device specially designed to apply tension forces to the sheets during the rolling, in order to produce a uniaxial molecular orientation in the samples. Rollers with 120 mm diameter and 150 mm length were used. They were heated with an internal cartridge heater at 60°C. PBS sheets were drawn to various draw ratios (from 0 to 4.1) at a constant draw rate of 1 rpm. The draw ratio (λ) was defined as the ratio of the length after (L) to the length before (L_o) rolling. L was determined from the displacement in the ink marks drawn on the surfaces of the sheets.

Characterization

Density at 25°C was obtained using a saturated solution of sodium bromide in a density gradient column, following the Japanese JIS K 7112 standard.

The properties of PBS under tension stresses were characterized by using an UTM-111-10T Orientec Co, Ltd. tensile testing machine. Stress-strain curves were obtained and the Young's modulus and tensile strength were determined. Samples have a thickness of 0.05 to 0.1 mm and 6 mm width. A load cell of 20 kg and a gauge length of 35.0 mm were used; the crosshead speed was set to 10 mm/min, and a range of 100 % strain at 25 °C was recorded. An oven was used to obtain measurements at different temperature (40-80°C).

The crystallinity of the rolled PBS samples was obtained from wide-angle X-ray diffraction. Diffractograms were recorded using CuKα radiation in a RAD-C instrument (Rigaku Denki Co). The X-ray diffractometer operated at 40 kV and 35 mA for 40 minutes. WAXD equatorial and meridian scan intensity profiles were obtained.

Differential scanning calorimetry (DSC) was performed in a Thermo plus DSC 8230, (Rigaku Co., Japan) calorimeter. All experiments were carried out under dry nitrogen atmosphere. 10-15 mg samples were used and the heating rate was set to 20°C/min. The melting temperature (T_m) and melting enthalpy (ΔH_m) of the samples were obtained from DSC thermograms.

Dynamic mechanical thermal (DMA) analyses were carried out using a two-point bending mode system (Rheovibron DDV-II-EA, Orientec Co). Measurements were obtained at a heating rate of 2°C/min in the temperature range from –150 to 150°C. The glass transition temperature (T_g) was obtained as the maximum temperature of the tan δ vs. temperature curves. Experiments were carried out at a frequency of 1 Hz and the measurements were obtained in the region of linear viscoelasticity.

The shrinkage of the rolled PBS samples was measured using in the temperature range from 25 to 150°C; a heating rate of 2°C/min and a distance between jaws of 60 mm were used. The shrinkage percentage was obtained as the difference between the final (L) and initial (L_o) distance. The Haze percentage (%) of the rolled samples was obtained in a Digital Haze Computer, SUGA Test Instruments HGM-2DP. The tests were conducted at room temperature.

Sonic velocity modulus was evaluated using a sonic propagation method at room temperature using a pulse propagation meter Rheovibron DDV-5-B (Orientec Co.). Pulse frequency was 10 kHz and pulse propagation distance between sending and receiving the sonic pulse was generally 250-300 mm (100-150 mm in some cases). The sonic modulus (E_s) was calculated from the sonic velocity (c) and density (ρ) by using the following relationship:

$$E_s = c^2\rho$$

The sonic velocity was obtained from the propagation time vs. sample length plot.

Results and Discussion

The mechanical properties of the PBS samples with a draw ratio of 1, i.e. unrolled samples, were characterized by using stress-strain experiments at different temperatures (Figure 1). The increase in the temperature produces a decrease in stress of PBS for a giving strain, but all curves show the same behavior. There is a sudden increase in stress for low strain values, followed by the flow of the polymer chains in the plastic region; finally the samples are broken. PBS shows a high elongation at break, independently of the temperature but the higher the temperature, the lower the Young's modulus (Figure 2). A temperature of 60°C was selected to apply rolling stress by using different draw ratios. The PBS sheets were treated in the rolling machine to induce uniaxial molecular orientation. The draw ratios used vary between 1.1 and 4.1.

Figure 3 shows the stress-strain curves of rolled PBS sheets under different draw ratios. The roller treatment increased the tensile strength, Young's modulus and yield stress of PBS sheets, but the elongation at break steadily decreases. Draw ratios higher than 2.6 produce the most noticeable changes in mechanical properties. Those trends in the mechanical properties are related to modifications in the molecular orientation and crystallinity of the PBS sheet.

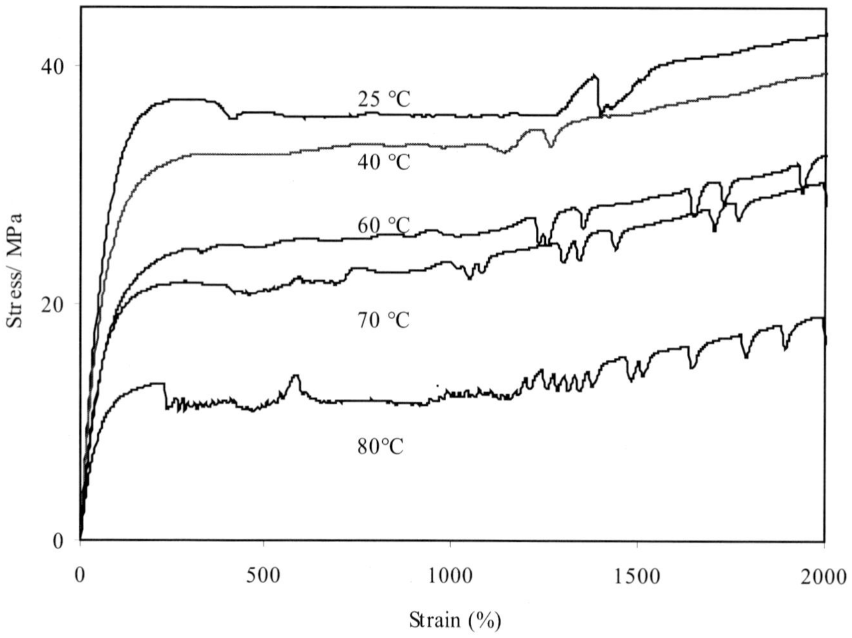

Figure 1. Stress-strain curves of unrolled PBS sheets measured at different temperatures.

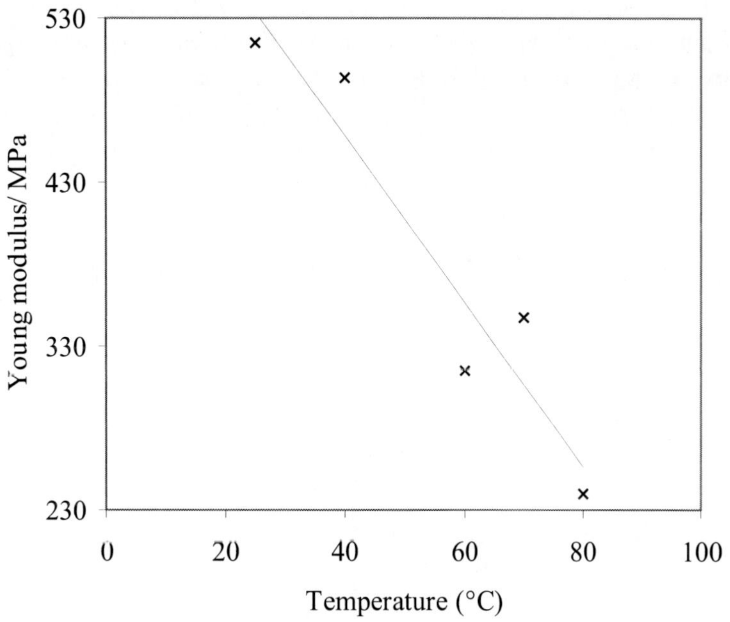

Figure 2. Young's modulus of unrolled PBS sheets measured at different temperature.

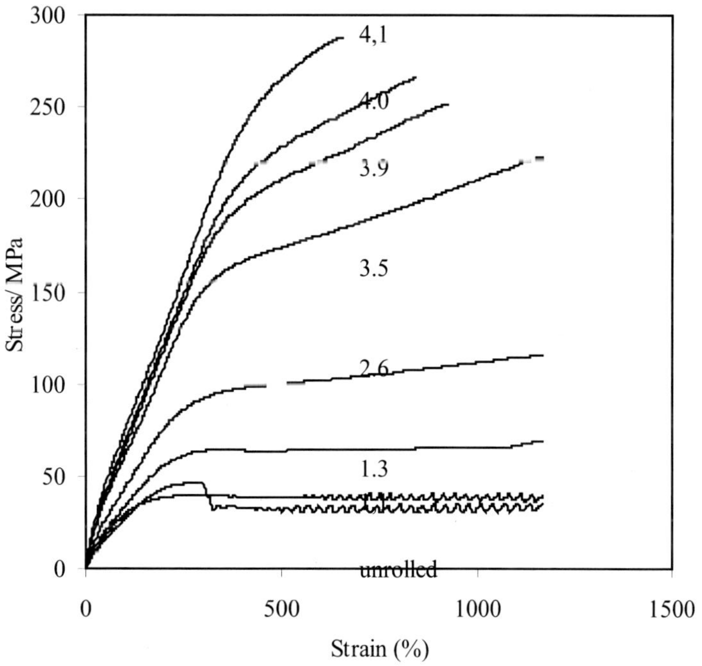

Figure 3. Stress-strain curves of rolled PBS sheets at different draw ratios. Numbers indicate the draw ratio (λ).

Changes in the crystallinity of PBS after rolling were obtained using X-ray diffraction. Figure 4 shows flat – film patterns for the unrolled PBS; in fact the Debye rings indicates that PBS is an isotropic material, which becomes highly oriented as the draw ratio increases (mainly for draw ration higher than 2.6). Moreover, the X-Ray diffractograms (WAXD) for equatorial and meridian scans (Figures 5a and 5b, respectively) shows the presence of crystals in the PBS (2θ = 18-28 degrees), and the higher the draw ratio, the higher the crystallinity in the PBS.

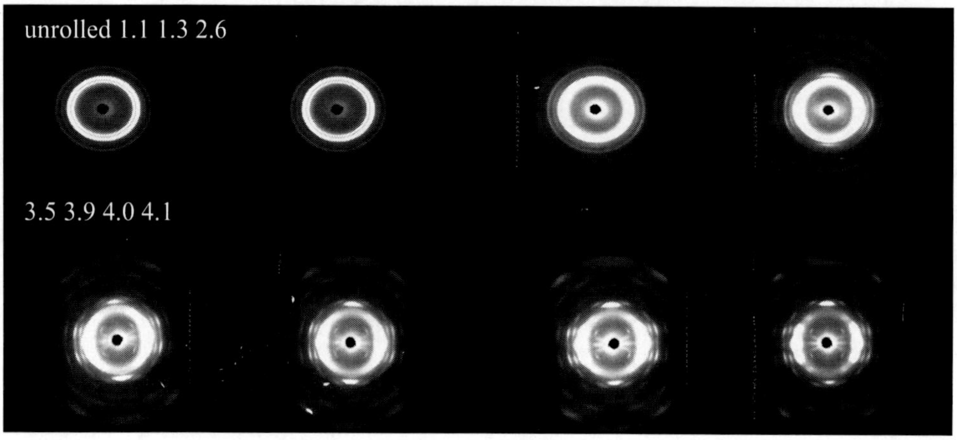

Figure 4. WAXD patterns of rolled PBS sheets at various draw ratios. Drawing direction is vertical. Numbers indicated the draw ratio (λ).

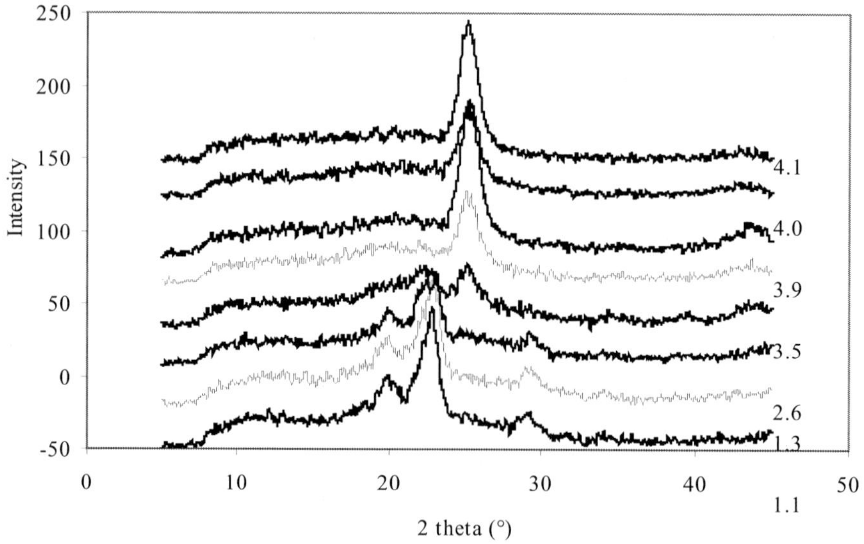

Figure 5a. WAXD equatorial scan intensity profiles of rolled PBS sheets at various draw ratios. Numbers indicated the draw ratio (λ).

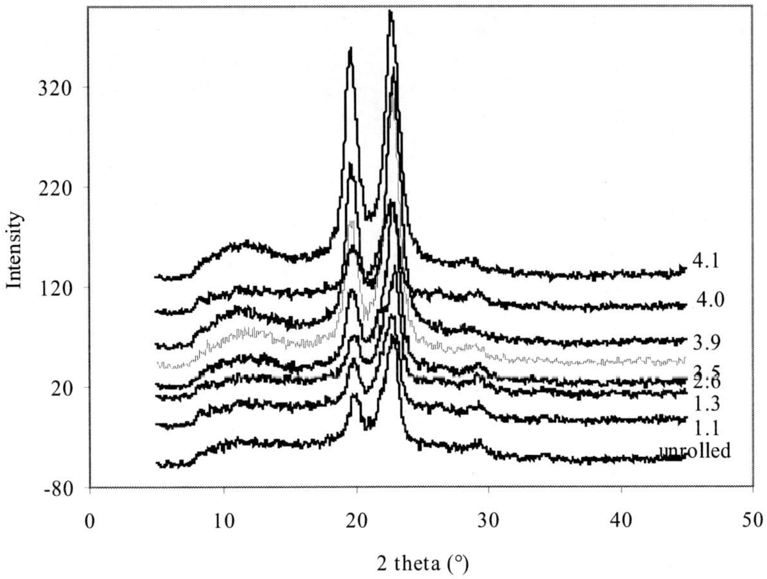

Figure 5b. WAXD meridian scan intensity profiles of rolled PBS sheets at various draw ratios.

The WAXD equatorial diffractograms of unrolled PBS show three peaks between 20 and 30 degrees. The rolling under low draw ratio removes these peaks and a new diffraction peak at 25 degrees appears for λ higher than 2.6. Therefore, the rolling process produces a molecular reorientation in the PBS polymer matrix and an increase in crystallinity, too. The WAXD meridian diffractograms of rolled PBS show different trend than the equatorial ones; in this case, the increase in the draw ratio increase the crystallinity of the PBS, but always the same pattern is obtained. Therefore, the rolling process of PBS at low draw ratios produces a different orientation of the crystals, depending on the direction under which the stress is applied, the differences are more marked by increasing the draw ratio (specially for variation of λ higher than 2.6).

The variation in crystallinity of the PBS after rolling produces an increase in density (Figure 6), and the higher the draw ratio, the higher the density.

DSC thermograms (Figure 7) shows two transitions between 100 and 120ºC in the melting process of rolled PBS. It can be suggested that the low endotherm corresponds to the melting of the original crystallites in the unrolled PBS and the high endotherm to the melting of the recrystallized ones. Consequently, two kinds of morphologically different crystallites are created in the rolled PBS by melting and recrystallization. In fact, Figure 8 shows the noticeable increase in the melting temperature and enthalpy of PBS after rolling. For draw ratios higher than 2.6, a greater increase in melting temperature and mainly in melting enthalpy is observed. These results agree with the results obtained from the stress-strain experiments and WAXD. In some cases, the shapes of the peaks were remarkably affected by rolling.

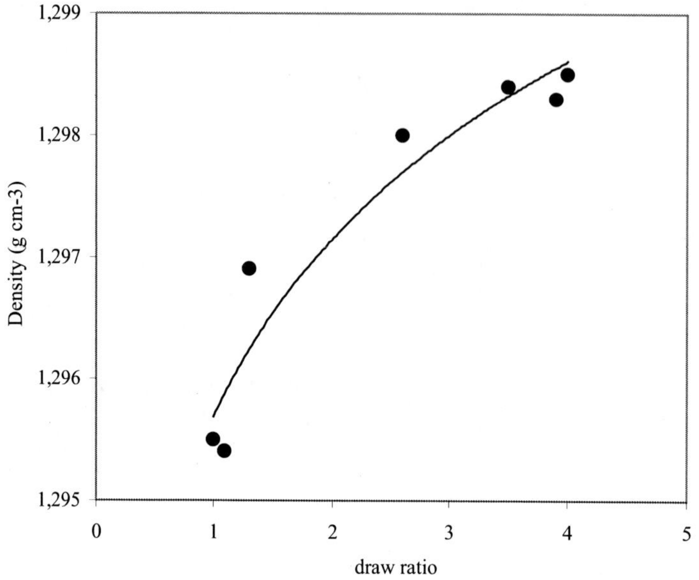

Figure 6. Density of rolled PBS samples as a function of the draw ratio.

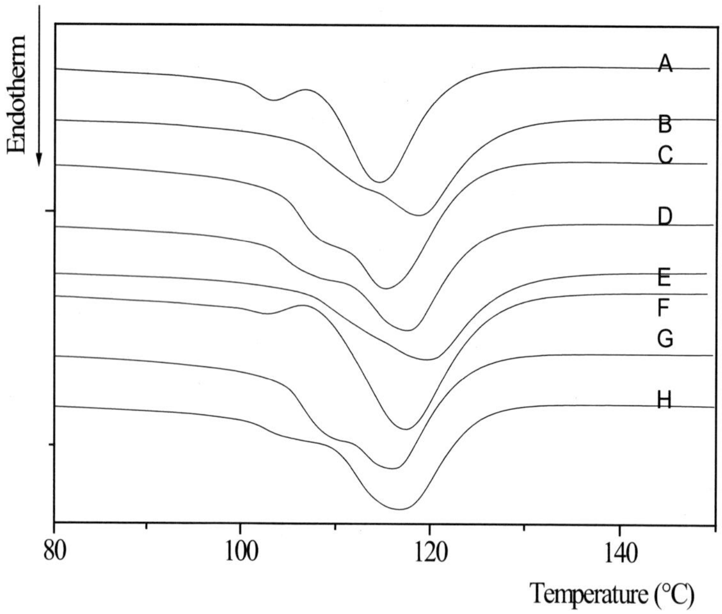

Figure 7. DSC thermograms of rolled PBS samples at various draw ratios: (A) as extruded, $\lambda = 1$, (B) $\lambda = 1.1$, (C) $\lambda = 1.3$, (D) $\lambda = 2.6$, (E) $\lambda = 3.5$, (F) $\lambda = 3.9$, (G) $\lambda = 4.0$, (H) $\lambda = 4.1$, from top to bottom.

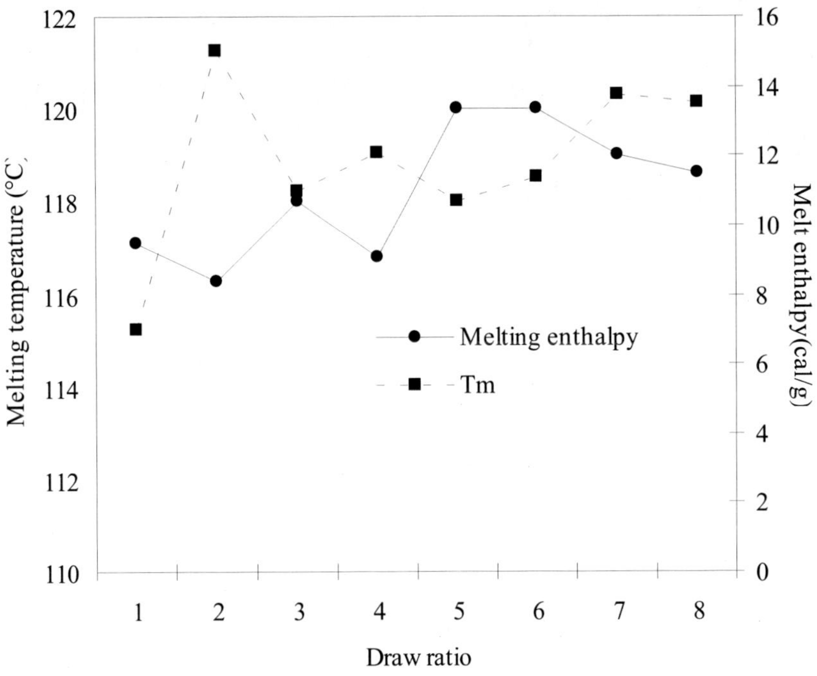

Figure 8. Variation of the melting temperature and enthalpy of rolled PBS samples as a function of the draw ratios.

DMA experiments provide information about the modifications produced in the rolled PBS sheets at low temperature. Figure 9a shows the variation of the storage modulus (E') as a function of the temperature for the rolled PBS sheets at different draw ratios. The elastic modulus increases by increasing the draw ratio in the rolled PBS sheets, in agreement with the stress-stain tests. Also the glass transition is observed at low temperature, although it is more clearly marked in Figure 9b. The T_g value increases by increasing the draw ratio due to the increase in the order of the PBS structure by rolling. The tan δ value at the maximum and the area under the tan δ curve (Figure 9b) decrease by increasing the draw ratio, indicating higher crystallinity in the rolled PBS sheet. There is a linear variation of T_g as a function of the draw ratio during rolling of PBS (Figure 10).

The shrinkage of PBS sheets after heating was also measured using DMA. Figure 11 shows a low degree of shrinkage of rolled PBS sheets at low draw ratio, but by increasing the draw ratio the degree of shrinkage dramatically raises. It is a consequence of the molecular orientation and improved crystallinity of PBS sheet induced by rolling.

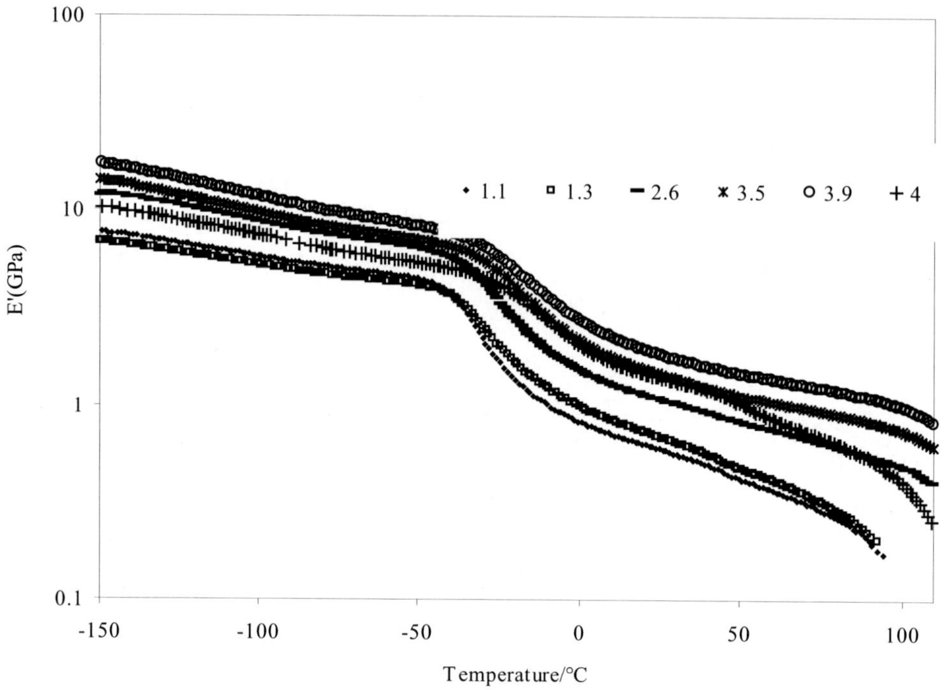

Figure 9a. Variation of the storage modulus as a function of the temperature in the rolled PBS rolled samples at various draw ratios. Frequency = 1 Hz.

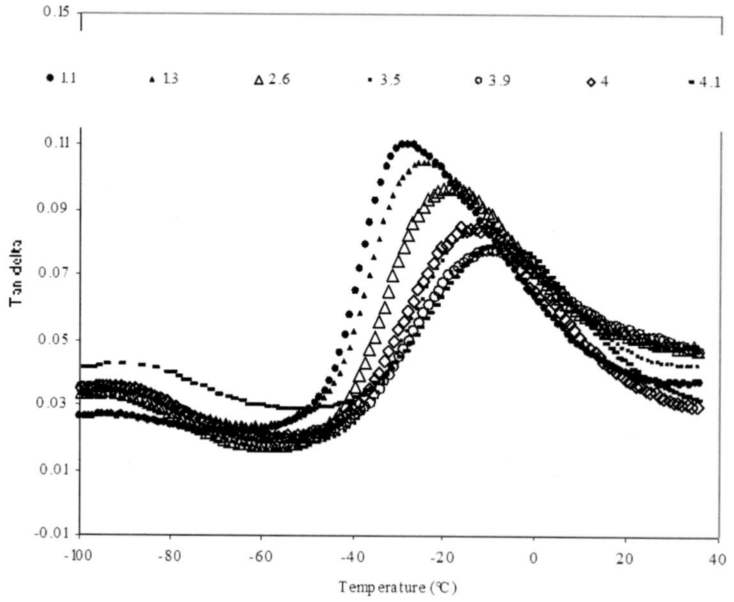

Figure 9b. Variation of the tan δ as a function of the temperature in the rolled PBS rolled samples at various draw ratios. Frequency = 1 Hz.

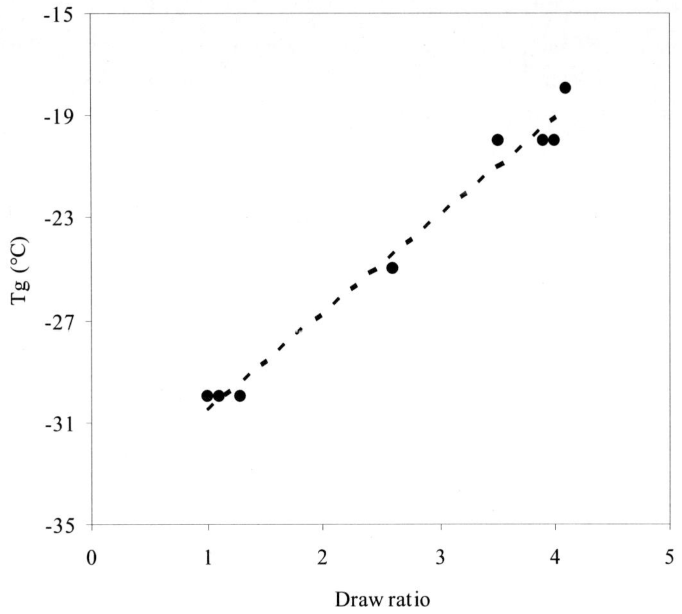

Figure 10. Variation of the glass transition temperature (T_g) as a function of the draw ratio for rolled PBS sheets.

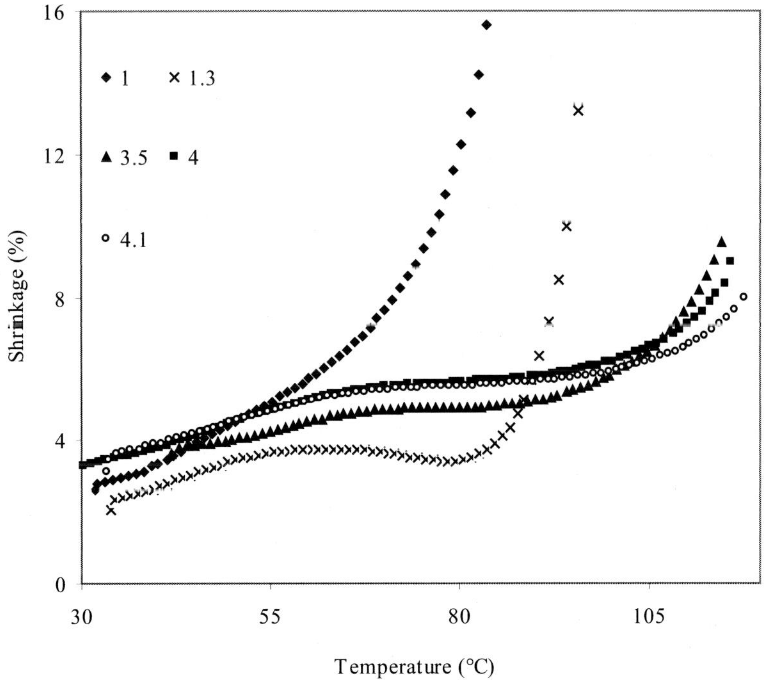

Figure 11. Degree of shrinkage of rolled PBS sheets as a function of temperature as a function of the draw ratio.

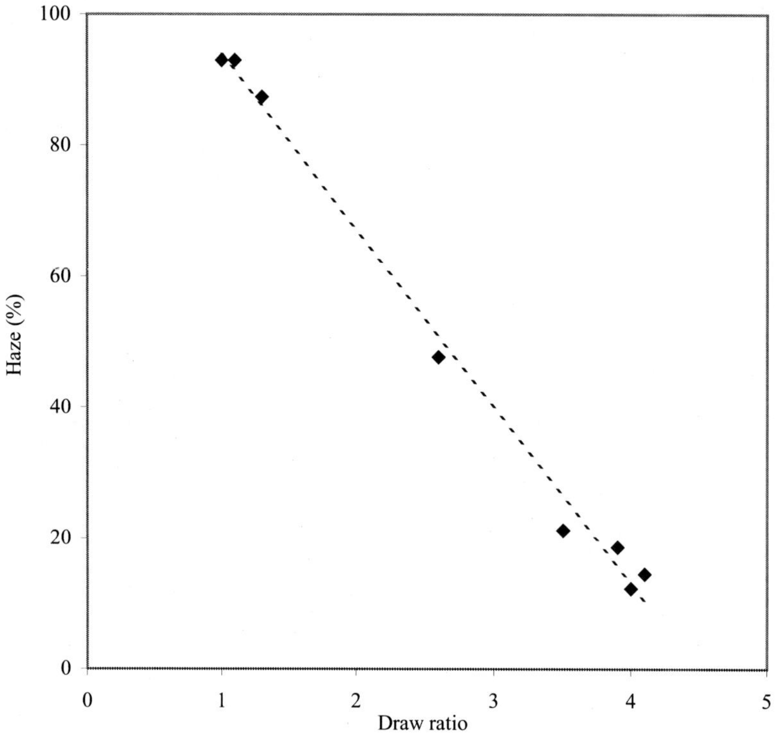

Figure 12. Haze percentage in rolled PBS sheets as a function of the draw ratio.

Variation in the crystallinity of the polymers affects their transparency. Rolled PBS sheets are white at low draw ratio, but they became transparent by increasing the draw ratio. In fact, the Haze percentage of rolled PBS linearly decreases by increasing the draw ratio (Figure 12) indicating that rolling decreases the scattering of visible light of PBS sheet, resulting in improved transparency as a result of the reorientation of the spherulitic structure to produce oriented lamellae. The higher the draw ratio, the higher the degree of molecular reorientation and the higher the transparency.

The crystallinity of the polymers also affects the propagation of sonic waves. Figure 13 shows the increase in the sonic modulus produced in rolled PBS sheets by increasing the draw ratio.

CONCLUSIONS

PBS rolled sheets with various draw ratios were obtained using a rolling mill machine. Rolling increased the T_g and crystallinity of PBS, more markedly for draw ratios higher than 2.6. Rolling also improved the mechanical and viscoelastic properties of PBS sheets. As a consequence the transparency and propagation of sonic waves in rolled PBS sheets was increased. Therefore, rolling can be used to improve and control the physical properties of PBS sheets.

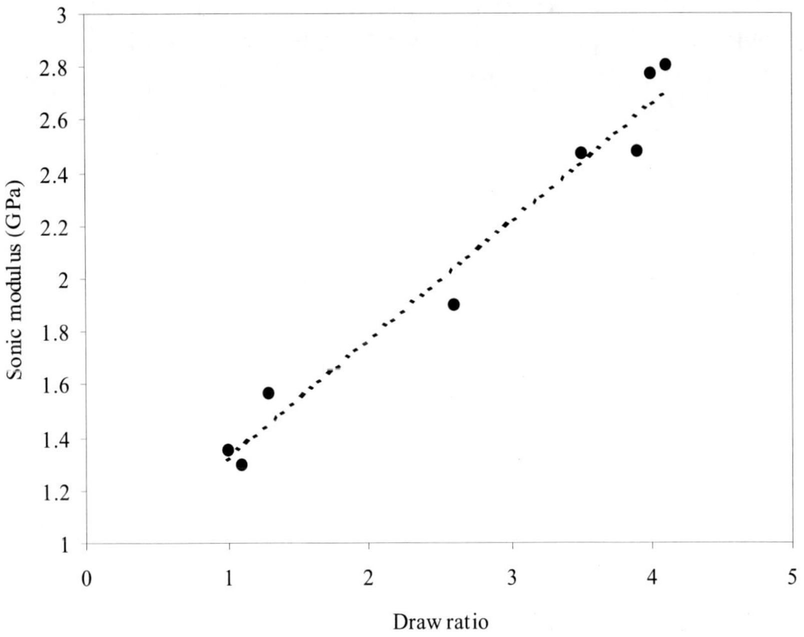

Figure 13. Variation of the sonic modulus in rolled PBS samples as a function of the draw ratio.

ACKNOWLEDGEMENTS

Financial support from the Universidad Nacional of Costa Rica, CONICIT-MICIT, the Ibero American Science and Technology Program (CYTED Network VIII.D), JICA of Japan, and the Adhesion and Adhesives Laboratory of the University of Alicante in Spain, is acknowledged.

REFERENCES

[1] Ehrig R.J., *Plastics Recycling, Products and Process*, Hanser, Munich, (1992).
[2] Qi K. and Nakayama K., *Polym. Polym. Composites*, 6 (7), (1998), 473.
[3] Mochizuki M., Nakayama K., Qian R., Jiang B., Hirami M., Hayashi T., Masuda T., and Nakajima A., *Pure & Appl. Chem.*, 69, (12), (1997), 2567.
[4] Qi K. and Nakayama K., *Polym. Polym. Composites*, 8 (3), (2000), 187.
[5] Reckmans B., Nakayama K., *J. Appl. Polym. Sci.*, 62, (1996), 247.
[6] Hayashi T., Nakayama K., Mochizuki M., Masuda T., *Pure Appl. Chem.*, 74 (5), (2002), 869.
[7] Nakayama, K., Masuda, T., Cao, A., Vega-Baudrit, J., Pereira, R., *Polym. Polym. Composites*, 11 (1), (2003), 51.
[8] Takashi, M., Amin, C., Nakayama, K., Suzuki, K., Katayama, H., *Agency for Industrial Science and Technology*, Japan; Daicel Chemical Industries, Ltd., Jpn. Kokai Tokkyo Koho, JP 2002105186 A2 20020410, Patent written in Japanese. (2002).
[9] Elberaichi, A. and David, C., *Eur. Polym. J.*, 37, (2001), 19.

[10] Jayasekara, R., Sheridan, S., Lourbakos, E., Beh, H., Christie, G.B.Y., Jenkins, M., Halley, P.B., Mc Glashan, S., and Lonergan, G.T., *Int. Biodet. Biodeg.*, 51, (2003), 77.
[11] Vega-Baudrit, J., Pereira, R., Nakayama, K., Masuda, T., Cao, A., *Polym. Polym. Composites*, 12 (1), (2004), in press.

In: New Developments in Polymer Analysis, Stabilization... ISBN 1-59454-511-1
Editors: G.E. Zaikov and A. Jiménez, pp. 71-83

Chapter 6

MECHANICAL AND THERMAL CHARACTERIZATION OF HIGH IMPACT POLYSTYRENE-POLYPROPYLENE BLENDS

D. Di Rienzo and J. M. Kenny,
University of Perugia at Terni. Loc. Pentima Bassa, 21 – 05100, Terni, Italy
F. Parres, J. López and R. Balart
Department of Mechanical and Materials Engineering. Polytechnic University of Valencia. Paseo Viaducto, 1 03801 Alcoy (Spain). e-mail: fraparga@dimm.upv.es

ABSTRACT

Behaviour of blends is very important to obtain new materials with optimum properties, the same as metallic alloys. This study analyses the variability of mechanical and thermal properties of high impact polystyrene (HIPS) with processing temperature and percentage of polypropylene (PP). Polystyrene and its derivatives are present in municipal solid wastes and sometimes, due to difficulties of separation processes, they can be contaminated with other commodities such us polypropylene. These materials also show some degradation because of previous processing and service life, which can induce a decrease on their performance. In this work, we have used raw HIPS and PP, so we can expect no previous degradation on materials. We have studied the influence of the presence of polypropylene as an impurity and how processing and reprocessing conditions can influence on ultimate properties of HIPS. Firstly, this work has focused on the study of variation of mechanical properties of samples with different amounts of polypropylene in order to observe a change in ultimate strength, Young modulus, Shore D hardness and impact strength. Secondly, we have studied changes on blends viscosity in order to optimize processing conditions and finally we have studied the influence of processing temperature and percentage of PP on glass transition temperature (Tg) as it is related to degradation processes.

Key words: High impact polystyrene, polypropylene, blends, mechanical properties, thermal degradation.

INTRODUCTION

During the last years, consumption of plastics has increased considerably due to the wide variety of properties that can be reached. This increase on consumption has generated simultaneously an associated problem: the presence of big amounts of wastes. The main problem for recycling all these wastes is separation since they appear mixed in municipal solid wastes. Polyolefins, such as polyethylene (LDPE, HDPE) and polypropylene (PP) and other commodities such as polystyrene and derivatives and PVC appear in big amounts in these wastes. It is impossible to recycle all them at once because each one shows different processing range, structure, degradation temperature and, of course, different properties, so it is important to separate them in order to optimize recycling processes and performance of recycled materials.

Moreover, we have to consider miscibility of polymers which is useful to establish interactions between them and improve their performance by making a homogeneous blend. Many polymers admit low amounts of impurities (or blended component) without significant changes on their properties but higher amounts drive to a partial miscible system or some times immiscible system. In these cases, performances of blends are considerably reduced.

So we can consider that separation processes are very important to obtain materials with balanced properties. In the last years, some efforts have been done in order to identify plastics which are marked with numbers or letters, but, even in this case, separation is not easy and very expensive. Recycling companies, to avoid separation processes, try to find wastes streams which are not mixed or contaminated with other plastics. These selected wastes show another advantage: they do not need to be washed as occurs on wastes coming from municipal solid wastes in which, remains of organic matter can be found. In the present work, we study mechanical and thermal properties of high impact polystyrene (HIPS) and polypropylene (PP) blends to find the optimum composition range.

Previously to this study we analyzed the nature and origin of these wastes. Polystyrene is widely used in a variety of applications due to an excellent combination of processing conditions, general properties (such as mechanical resistance) and low cost. It is used in packaging industry (compact disc boxes, foamed PS to protect products, packing of dairy products…) food industry (tablespoons), agricultural industry (gavels), textile (hangers and accessories). Wastes from these industries show important advantages. As they are obtained from raw materials, processing cycles are well-known and this situation allows to obtain a recycled material characterized by a high quality and little thermal degradation.

Some of these wastes present certain problems due to their nature. Some retired products can contain different impurities, such as inks, because of their use. In this case, they must be washed before recycling processes; for example, it is quite usual to find sand in wastes from gavels, and this must be removed. Sometimes, retired products (those which do not reach the standard) can appear mixed with other materials, which show similar characteristics and functionality, so the same product can be made of different materials, with similar features.

This is the case of hangers. They can be made of polypropylene (PP) although mostly of them are made of high impact polystyrene (HIPS). When collecting PS coming from hangers, some PP hangers can appear and this PP acts as a blending material and can affect to the ultimate performance of HIPS.

The same situation can be seen in containers of dairy products, such as yogurt, which are mainly made of HIPS but also sometimes PP can be used on certain products.

MECHANICAL BEHAVIOUR OF RECYCLED HIPS WASTES

As we can deduce from introduction, PS wastes coming from hangers have been subjected to previous processing cycles with different processing conditions. These wastes can also be mixed with some polyolefins which act as impurities. The presence of polyethylene (LDPE) can be attributed to the masterbatch used for coloring these materials and polypropylene (PP) can appear in small amounts since some hangers are made of it. Taking into account these considerations, in this work we analyse which is the influence of these factors on the ultimate performance of recycled HIPS.

Our study has focused on the study of the influence of processing temperature on degradation processes and the decrease on mechanical properties due to the presence of PP as inmiscible impurity.

Both processing and reprocessing cycles and PP content can reduce considerably mechanical performace of recycled HIPS. Also we have to consider the presence of an elastomeric phase (polybutadiene) which is very sensitive to temperature and can contribute to crosslinking processes.

We have used different processing temperatures in the range 210 – 290 ºC to determine the influence on mechanical behaviour due to degradation processes of PS phase or crosslinking process of polybutadiene. To study the influence of polypropylene on ultimate performance we prepared HIPS/PP blends with different PP content in the range 2.5 – 10 % wt. In both cases we analyzed their influence on mechanical properties such as tensile strength, elongation at break, Young modulus and impact strength, and also on thermal behaviour characterized by glass transition temperature (Tg) and crosslinking process of polybutadiene phase.

We performed tensile tests of all samples and we could observe that behaviour of all materials is very similar (Table 1). Elongation at break suffers certain variations but all samples present the same behaviour, tensile stress and Young modulus are very similar; the difference appears in the elongation at break, but it is not directly related with processing temperature.

Table 1. Variation of Different Tensile Properties with Processing Temperaure for HIPS

Processing Temperature [ºC]	Young modulus [MPa]	Tensile strength [MPa]	Elongation at break
210	1073	18,6	0,25
220	910	18,9	0,42
230	960	18,1	0,36
240	1126	18,2	0,30
250	915	19,9	0,44
270	944	19,9	0,37
290	1042	20,2	0,26

The other mechanical property analysed is impact strength. We used a Charpy pendulum (6J) to determine the energy absorbed by samples with different processing temperatures.

Figure 1 shows no significant variation of impact strength with processing temperature as observed in tensile tests. This situation is quite important because it means that processing temperature does not induce significant degradation levels on samples, and consequently no important changes on mechanical properties are observed. We have also studied variation of hardness by using Shore D method on samples with different processing temperatures (Figure 2). As it can be observed processing temperature does not affect hardness results.

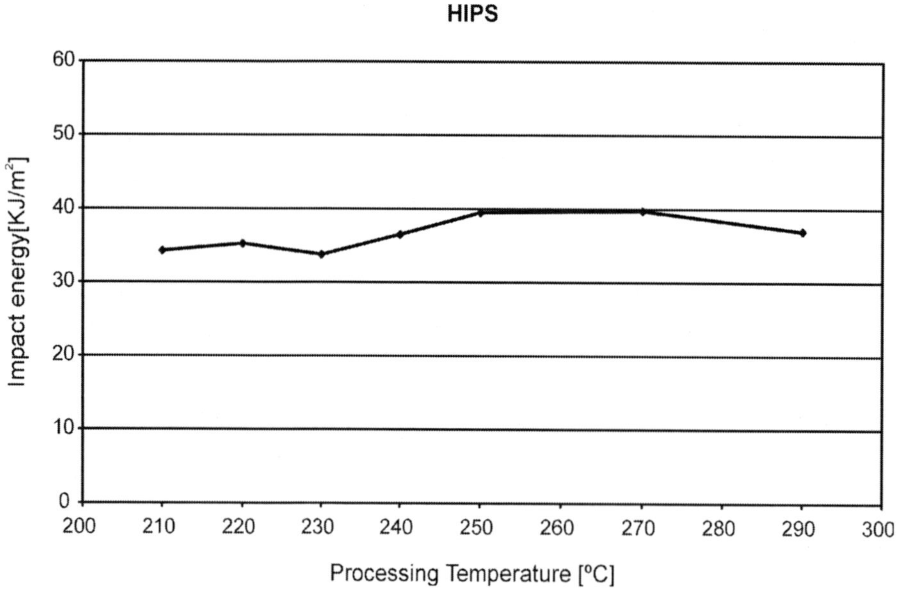

Figure 1. Variation of impact strength with processing temperature.

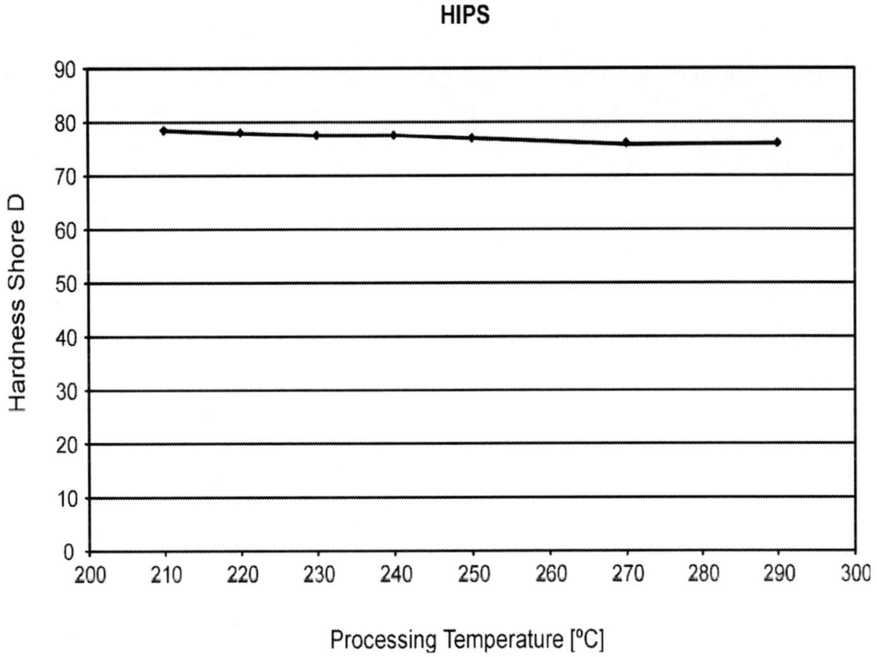

Figure 2. Variation of Shore D hardness with processing temperature.

We can conclude that processing temperature does not affect ultimate mechanical properties even ductile properties which are more sensitive to degradation processes. This conclusion is very important when working with recycled materials which have been subjected to different processing cycles with different temperature ranges.

Secondly we analysed the variation of mechanical properties with PP content since the presence of PP in PS wastes coming from hangers in quite frequent. Content of PP was varied from 2.5 to 10 % wt and we used two different processing temperatures.

As we can observe in Figures 3 & 4, ductile mechanical properties (as elongation at break) are considerably reduced with the amount of PP, while resistant mechanical properties (tensile strength, Young modulus) remain on similar values also for 220 ºC and 250 ºC as processing temperatures.

This situation can be due to a low adherence between the two components of the blend which are miscible. The interphase between PP and the HIPS matrix acts as stress concentrator which plays an important role in the fracture process.

Impact strength (Figure 5) suffers an important decrease independently of the processing temperature. This reduction can be attributed to the lack of adherence between PP and the HIPS matrix as described before.

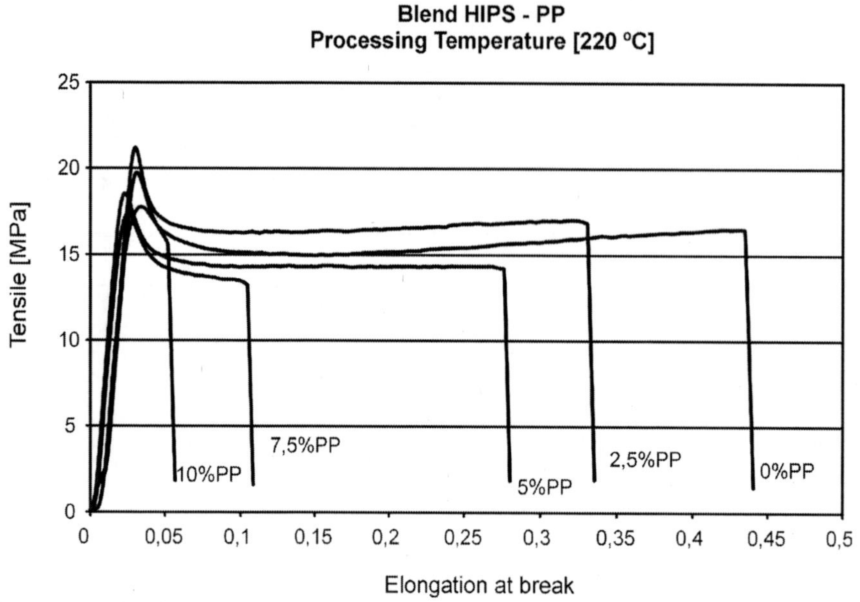

Figure 3. Stress-strain diagrams of different HIPS/PP blends with a processing temperature of 220 °C.

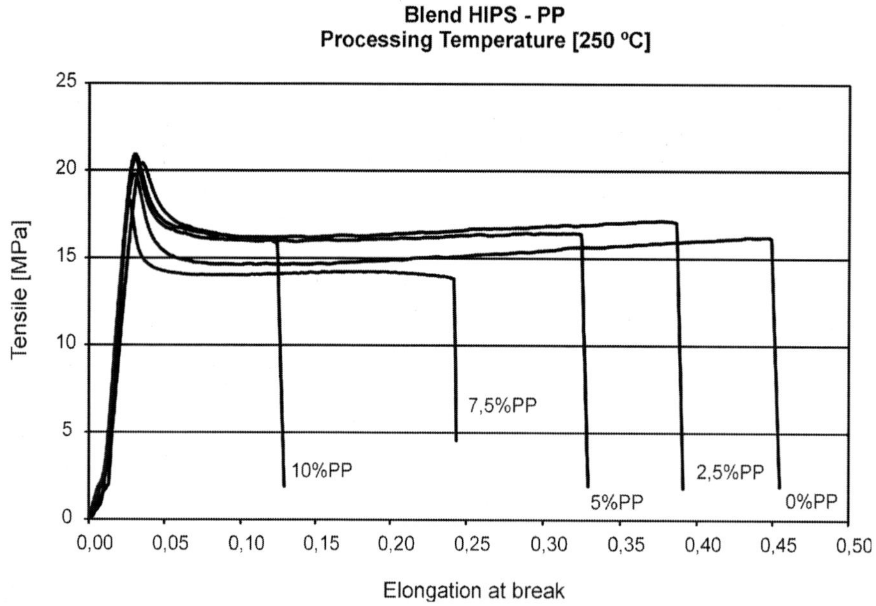

Figure 4. Stress-strain diagram of different HIPS/PP blends with a processing temperature of 250 °C.

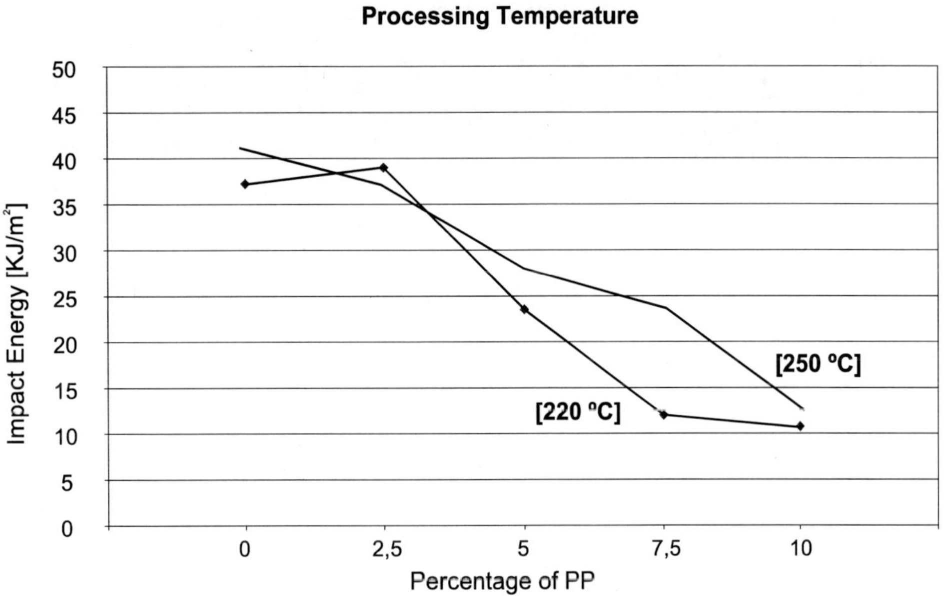

Figure 5. Variation of impact strength with % wt PP.

Rheological Properties on HIPS/PP Blends

It is important to make a rheological study of materials since we are working with wastes that can accumulate some degradation levels due to previous processing cycles and service life. This can induce some changes on rheological properties and can influence reprocessing and ultimate properties. Otherhand, the immiscible phase, polypropylene, can act as a plasticizer. We studied the influence of processing temperature and polypropylene content on material viscosity. It is important to know samples viscosity since it can be very useful for an optimum material processing. A standard MFI plastometer was used to determine the melt flow index of different samples.

Thermal degradation is an important factor to be considered since it can highly affect the behaviour of recycled material. This degradation can be attributed to a reduction of chains length due to the breaking of C-C bonds. This situation can cause a reduction on mechanical properties (mainly ductile properties). Previous degradation levels can be characterized by using MFI test. Degraded samples flow easier than non-degraded ones. We performed MFI tests on samples by using different conditions in the heating cylinder which varies in the range 210 °C-290 °C (Figure 6).

In Figure 6 we can observe that MFI values remain constant until 250 °C, higher temperatures produce an important increase on MFI. This phenomenon appears at high temperatures in the range 250-270 °C. In contrast MFI remains constant at 220 °C. This situation can be attributed to a decrease on chains length as described previously, which is more intense at high temperatures.

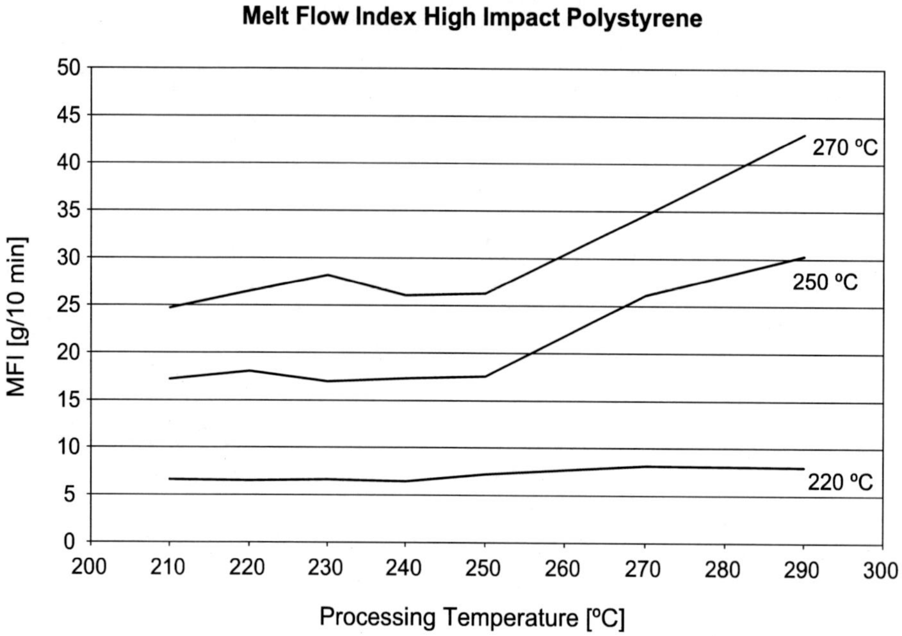

Figure 6. Variation of MFI with processing temperature of HIPS.

Secondly, the experience focused on the study of samples with different polypropylene content. As can be observed in Figure 7, PP acts as an internal plasticizer as a consequence of its immiscibility with the PS matrix. This situation can contribute to improve flow during processing.

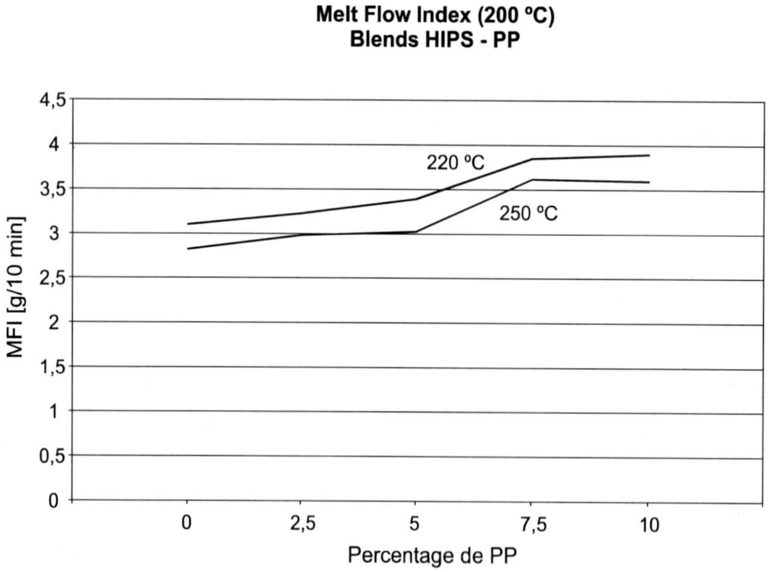

Figure 7. Variation of MFI with % wt PP.

Morphological Study of Fracture Surface

The morphological study was carried out by using scanning electron microscopy (SEM) to establish the relationship between fracture morphology and mechanical properties. The analysis of fracture surfaces of HIPS with different processing temperatures (Figures 8 & 9) shows no significant changes on morphology with processing conditions.

Figure 8. Micrography of fracture surface of HIPS processed at 210 °C (500 x).

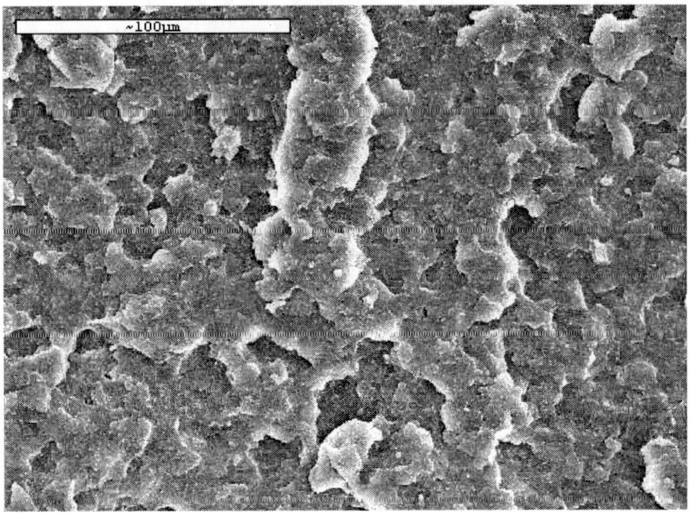

Figure 9. Micrography of fracture surface of HIPS processed at 230 °C (500 x).

But when we observe micrographies of samples with different PP content, we can see some differences on fracture surface (Figure 10 & 11).

We can observe some spheres and voids generated by their absence immersed on a HIPS matrix. The amount of these spheres and voids increases with PP content and play an important role during fracture processes as they act as stress concentrators due to the lack of miscibility/adherence with the styrenic component.

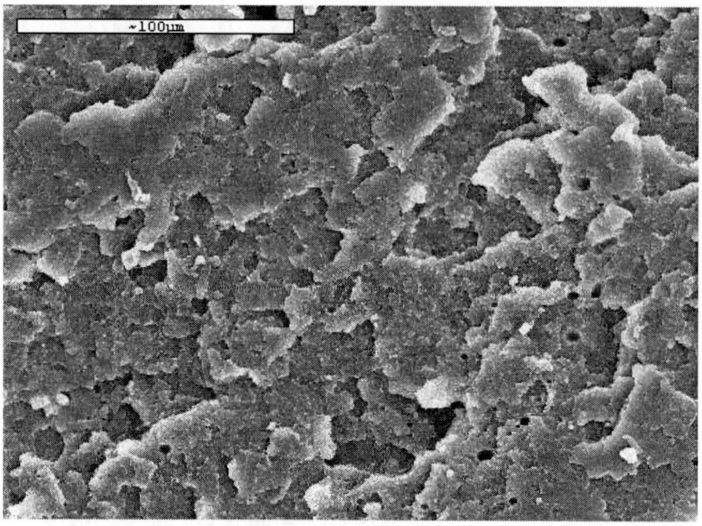

Figure 10. Micrography of fracture surface of HIPS contaning 2.5 wt % PP processed at 220 °C (500 x).

Figure 11. Micrography of fracture surface of HIPS contaning 10 wt % PP processed at 220 °C (500 x).

Characterization of Degradation Level by Thermal Analysis

Degradation level of materials can also be followed by means of differential scanning calorimetry (DSC) that gives information of thermal changes (glass transition temperature, Tg, basically) as a consequence of the degradation processes experimented by the material. Figure 12 shows the variation of Tg with processing temperature. It can be observed a small decrease of Tg with processing temperature which can be attributed to the plasticization efect of degradation, since degradation involves a reduction on chain length (with much more mobility) and this performs a reduction on Tg.

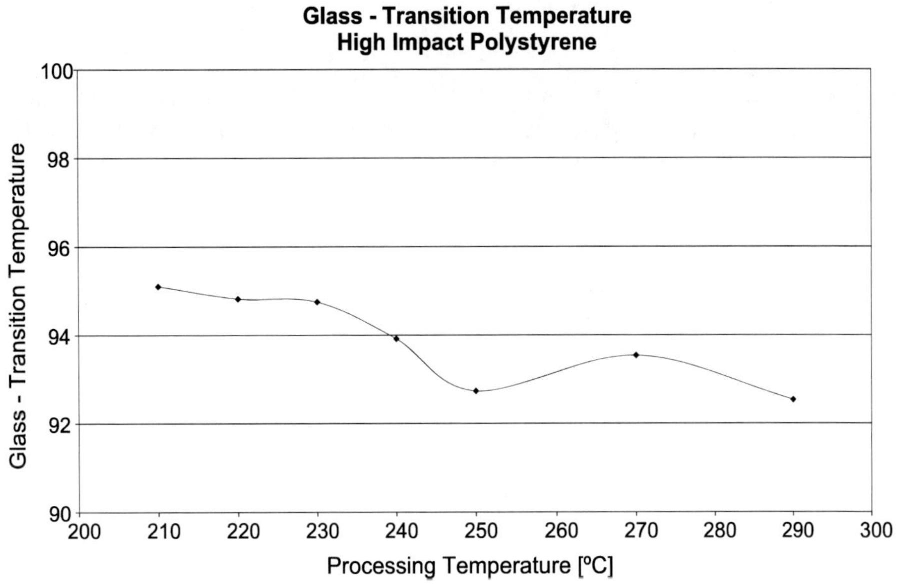

Figure 12. Variation of Tg for different processing temperature.

Previous processing cycles and processing conditions affect crosslinking process experimented by polybutadiene since it is an irreversible process (Figure 13). High processing temperatures contribute to lower crosslinking onset temperature due to the presence of free radicals that accelerate crosslinking process. This process can be used for determining thermal history accumulated by material.

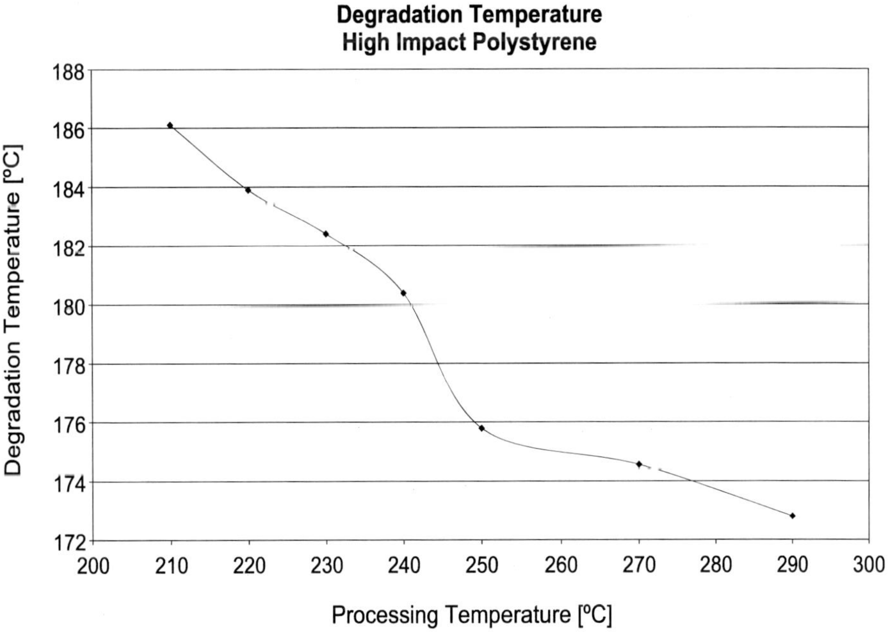

Figure 13. Variation of onset crosslinking temperature for polybutadiene phase at different processing temperatures.

Conclusions

Wastes from PS hangers are often mixed with different types of impurities than can influence on the reprocessing of these materials and on their ultimate performance. These wastes are sensitive to different factors:

- Previous processing cycles and service life which can contribute to certain degradation levels.
- The presence of an elastomeric phase, polybutadiene, highly sensitive to temperature, needs to be considered since temperature can cause crosslinking processes.
- The presence of immiscible impurities, such as polypropylene, can reduce considerably the interaction in the blends reducing considerably the mechanical performance.

Mechanical properties do not suffer remarkable changes with processing temperature. On the other hand, an increase on PP content causes important changes. Regarding tensile and other mechanical parameters, PP produces a decrease in the elongation at break (and other ductile properties), remaining invariable the elastic modulus and tensile strength. Impact strength shows a high decrease due to PP presence with percentage higher than 2.5% wt. Both, previous degradation and PP content perform a decrease on viscosity due to a reduction on chains length and a plasticization action respectively.

We can conclude that it is possible to obtain materials from PS wastes with balanced properties, mechanical, thermal and rheological. It is important to quantify previous degradation level accumulated and impurities content which will determine ultimate quality and performace of recycled material.

Acknowledgments

The authors thank "Ministerio de Ciencia y Tecnología", (Ref. PETRI: 95-0750.OP.02) for financial support.

References

[1] López J., Balart R., Sánchez L., Nadal A., *Polymer Analysis and Degradation*, *11:12* 181-192 (2000).

[2] Brennan LB., Isaac DH., Arnold JC., *Journal of Applied Polymer Science*, *86:3* 572 – 578 (2002).

[3] Fortelny I., Krulis Z., Michalkova D., *Polimery*, *47:7* 534 – 537 (2002).

[4] Fang ZP., Zeng MF., Cai GP., Xu CW., *Journal of Applied Polymer Science, 82:12* 2947 – 2952 (2001).

[5] Xu B., Simonsen J., Rocherfort WE., *Journal of Applied Polymer Science, 79:3* 418 – 425 (2001).

In: New Developments in Polymer Analysis, Stabilization... ISBN 1-59454-511-1
Editors: G.E. Zaikov and A. Jiménez, pp. 85-100

Chapter 7

RECYCLING OF PLASTIC WASTES COMING FROM ELECTRICAL AND ELECTRONICS INDUSTRY

R. Balar, [*] ***J. López, M. D. Salvador, L. Sánchez and D. García***
Department of Mechanical and Materials Engineering. Polytechnic University of Valencia. Paseo Viaducto, 1 03801 Alcoy (Spain) e-mail: rbalart@mcm.upv.es

ABSTRACT

In the last years, engineering plastics have acquired great relevance due to the excellent performances that can be reached, with enormous interest in engineering applications. Electrical and electronics industry is one of the big consumers of engineering plastics, generating at the same time, a big amount of wastes coming from these materials. These waste show good balance of different properties after their service life. One of the most used plastic in engineering applications is poly(acrylonitrile-butadiene-styrene), ABS due to the excellent combination of mechanical, thermal and processing properties and specially, low cost. Other engineering plastic, widely used in electrical and electronics industry is polycarbonate which contributes to an excellent toughness and thermal resistance. An interesting possibility of recycling these wastes is based on the preparation of physical mixtures or blends. These blends allow carrying out recycling processes of some materials that would not be recycled in an individual way, due to the low volumes of wastes generated and processing difficulties if compared with commodities. This is the case of polycarbonate. Preparation of blends according to the ratio, in which these plastics are generated, can represent a solution to the recovery of these materials. Also, the technical nature of these wastes can contribute to obtain recycled materials with an excellent combination of mechanical, thermal and processability properties.

Key words: Polycarbonate; ABS; Degradation; Blends; Recycling.

---

* Corresponding author.

INTRODUCTION

Plastics have progressively invaded all industrial sectors and at the moment they play a decisive role in applications of high engineering content which require a good combination of mechanical, thermal and chemical characteristics, and specially, low weight. All these features can be reached, in many cases, by using engineering and high performance plastics. Wastes generated in these sectors of high technology content (automotive, electrical and electronics, aeronautics, naval, ...) are materials that even at the end of their service life maintain good properties.

There are many industrial activities that absorb high amounts of engineering and high performance plastics. Electrical and electronics equipment industry is one of the most interesting because of the low reposition time of most of its products. This industry includes all type of appliances, TV, video and audio equipment, information technologies, telecommunication, illumination, toys, instruments, control panels and many others. The nature of the plastics used in this industry includes commodities, engineering and high performance plastics, but in a similar way as occurs in solid urban wastes, it is possible to find some groups of materials which are used in more extension than the rest. Plastics that represent a bigger ratio in the wastes from electrical and electronics equipment (WEE) are the following: an styrenic plastic, poly(acrylonitrile-butadiene-styrene), ABS, characterized by easy processability and improved impact and chemical resistance, and the other one is polycarbonate, which can be considered one of the most interesting engineering plastics due to its excellent thermal stability, toughness and high resistance to environmental agents. It is possible to find them in an individual way or mixed in different commercial blends which appear in parts of TV equipment, mobile and fixed telephony, parts of computers, toys, appliances, laboratory devices. It is possible to find commercial blends of these materials which cover a wide field of properties (mechanical resistance, stiffness and thermal stability).

On the other hand, recycling of engineering plastics is not as simple as that of poliolefins and styrenics for different reasons. Firstly, the amount of these wastes is notably lower than that of commodities; this situation represents difficulties to reach economical viability of the recycling processes. Secondly, taking into account technical considerations, processing conditions of engineering plastics are substantially more complex than those of commodities, since they require high processing temperatures, more complex refrigeration systems, previous drying and, sometimes, processing equipment with more performances than typical ones. These circumstances hinder greatly the industrial recovery of these materials.

Recycling of ABS is quite easy due to its relatively low cost, because of the high levels of consumption. ABS also shows an excellent processability. All this, makes recycling process of ABS highly viable also from technical and economical point of view, in a similar way to that of polyolefins. Nevertheless, polycarbonate is a high cost engineering plastic in comparison to ABS and its processing systems is more complex, with problems of moisture, high processing temperatures, more complex refrigeration systems and different screw geometries.

Considering the previous and that the generation ratio of wastes of ABS and PC is near to 4:1, an interesting possibility, also developed with success with poliolefins coming from solid urban wastes, is the preparation of physical mixtures or blends in the range of compositions near to the ratio in which these materials appear in wastes from electrical and electronics equipment, since it makes possible the recovery of polycarbonate which is not attractive to industrial initiatives.

STUDY OF THE PREVIOUS DEGRADATION OF THE PLASTIC WASTES

When working with materials that have already been subjected to a previous transformation process and service life, it is convenient to carry out a quantification of the degradation level accumulated since it can influence processing conditions and mechanical and thermal properties.

ABS (Figure 1) is the component of the blends which is more susceptible of degradation than polycarbonate which can support thermal stresses during longer times and the action of the environmental agents although PC is more susceptible, as other polyesters, to hydrolysis processes in contact with the environmental moisture.

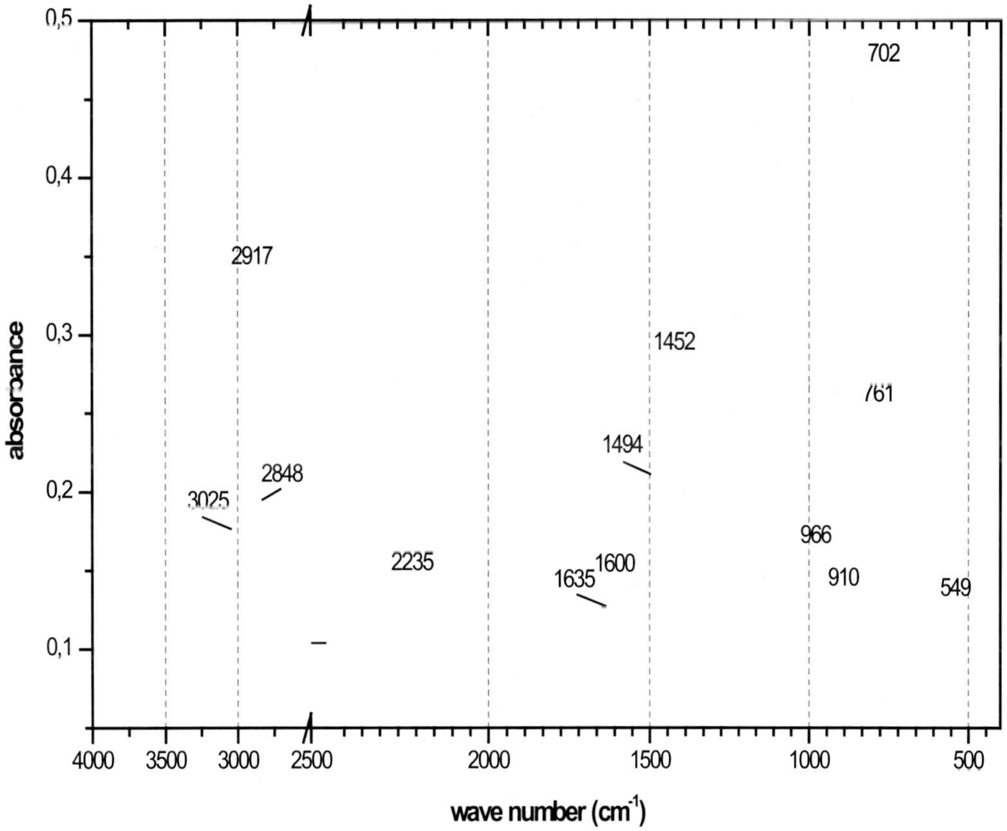

Figure 1. FTIR spectrum of a film of recycled ABS.

ABS and, especially polybutadiene phase disperse in the SAN matrix, is susceptible to suffer oxidative and thermo-oxidative degradation processes [1-2], associated to the degradation of polydienic structures by effect of temperature and contact with environmental agents, causing a decrease of the molecular weight and an increment of stiffness [3]. The elimination of hydrogens is responsible of the formation of radicals which form certain oxidation species in the presence of oxygen [4]. It is quite frequent the formation of hydroxyl radicals and in cases of higher oxidation, some carbonyl groups can be formed.

On the other hand, polycarbonate suffer thermo-oxidative processes [5-6] (Figure 2), is sensitive to light degradation and, especially, to hydrolysis degradation in contact with water (Figure 3). The most important of these degradation processes is hydrolysis since it is responsible of the formation of olygomers with a considerable decrease on molecular weight and its repercussion in the performances of the material. Thermo-oxidative processes are based on the oxidation and decomposition of the isophenyl groups present in polycarbonate structure. Next, a series of crosslinking reactions take place resulting in the formation of biphenyl groups through the joining with units of PC. At the end of the oxidation process, many olygomers can appear (which contribute to an important decrease in the molecular weight) where some acetophenona, benzyl alcohol, phenol and biphenol terminal groups of these olygomers can be appreciated.

Polycarbonate FTIR spectrum (Figure 4) does not show degradation species described previously, so we can expect no significant degradation levels. This is coherent with the behaviour of polycarbonates with excellent thermal and light resistance.

When working with plastic blends, the study of miscibility among different components acquires special relevance since it will condition greatly performances of these. Certain miscibility among the components of the blend contributes to a good interphase adherence and it performs an improvement of the performances.

MISCIBILITY OF POLYMERIC MATERIALS SYSTEMS

Miscibility of components of a blend can be studied by following the free energy (Gibbs expression) of the blend, where ΔG_m is defined as:

$$\Delta G_m = \Delta H_m - T \cdot \Delta S_m \tag{1}$$

In this expression, ΔH_m represents the blend enthalpy change, ΔS_m, entropy change and T the absolute temperature. To reach good miscibility between two polymers it is necessary a negative value for free energy of the blend ($\Delta G_m<0$). Usually, macromolecules entropy is very small due to the low possibilities of ordinations for species with high molecular weight, and as a consequence of it, many polymer systems are immiscible, resulting in two-phase systems where partial miscibility appears in each of the phases (Table 1).

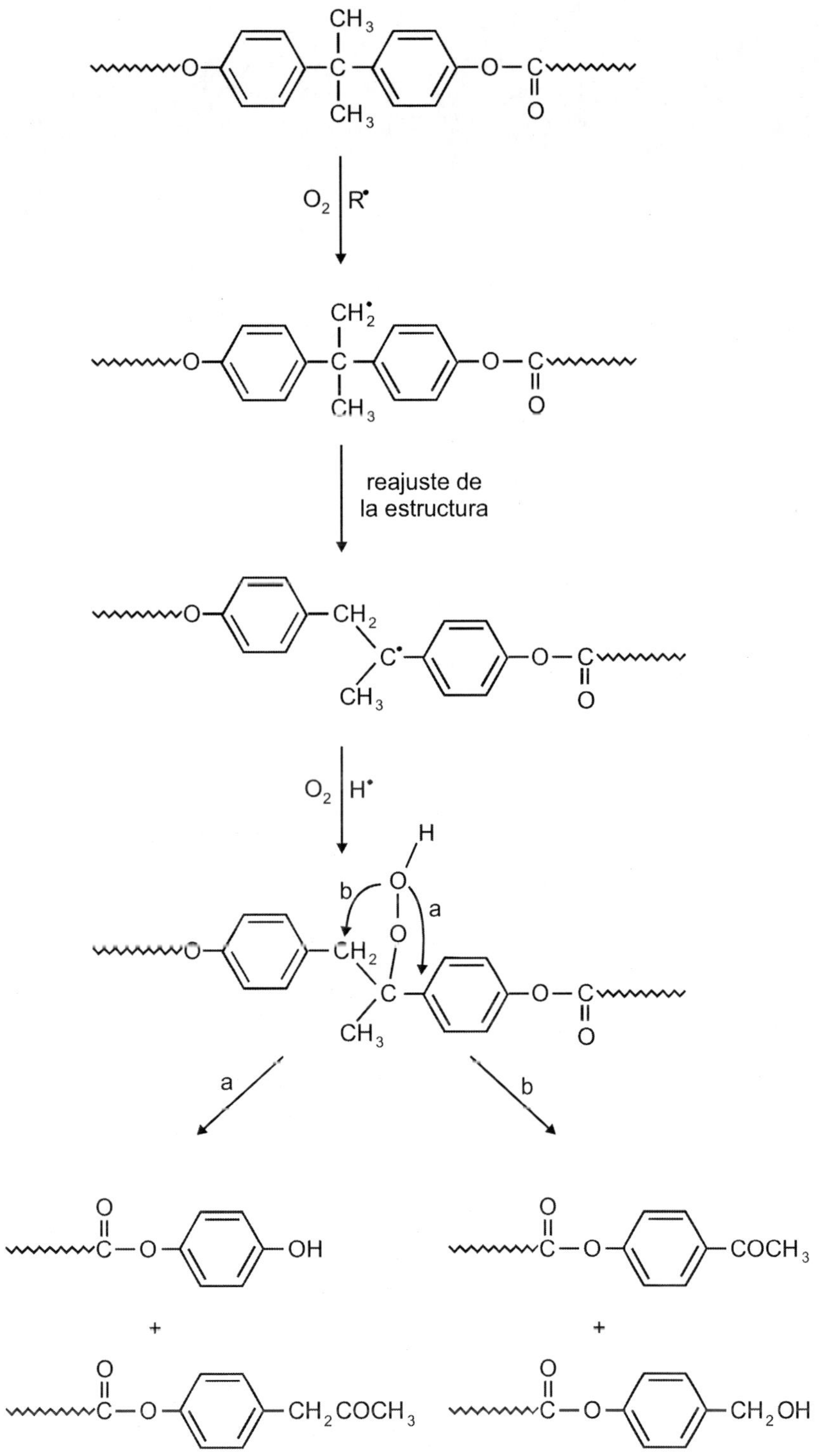

Figure 2. Scheme of thermo-oxidative degradation of polycarbonate with olygomer formation with several terminal groups.

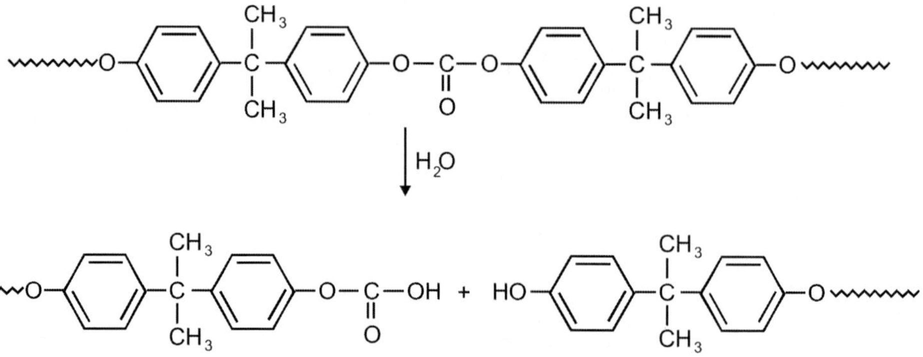

Figure 3. Scheme of hydrolysis degradation of polycarbonate.

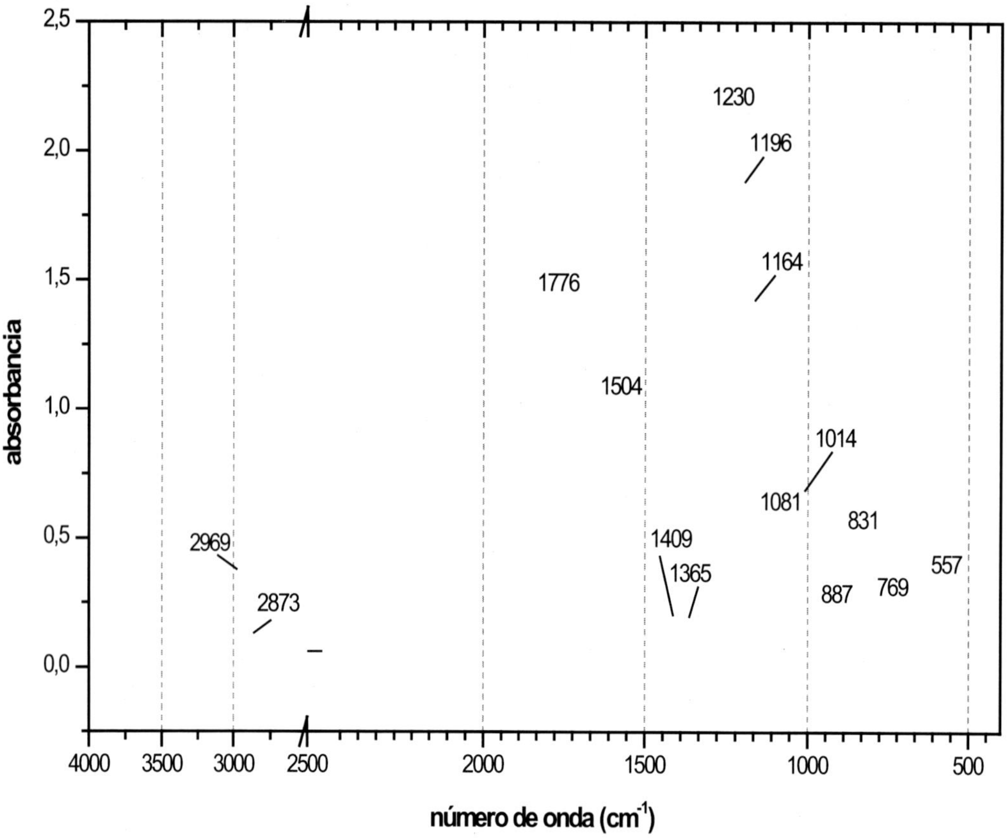

Figure 4. FTIR spectrum of a film of recycled polycarbonate, PC.

Table 1. Properties Optimized by Means of the Blending for Systems with Different Miscibility

Base polymer	Modifier polymer	Phases	Modified property
PVC	EVA	Miscible	Permanent plasticization
PVC	ABS	Partially miscible	Strength increment and processability
PVC	PMMA	Partially miscible	Strength increment and processability
PVC	α-MSAN	Miscible	HDT increment
HIPS	PPO	Miscible	Strength and HDT increment
ABS	PC	Partially miscible	Strength and HDT increment
ABS	Polisulfones	Immiscible	Strength and HDT increment
ABS	TPU	Depends on TPU	Hardness and durability increment
ABS	α-MSAN	Miscible	HDT increment
PMMA	PET	Immiscible	Lower cost and deformation
PC	Polyethylene	Immiscible	Energy absorption improvement

Miscibility of ABS and polycarbonate is limited as confirmed with the existence of two glass transitions corresponding to the rich phases in each one of the components of the blend (Figure 5). In spite of this, partial miscibility is enough to obtain a material which can be considered as an engineering material. Many authors [7-8] use the expression proposed by Fox, with certain modifications to determine the relationship of the Tg's of a blend.

$$\frac{1}{T_g} = \frac{w_1}{T_{g1}} + \frac{w_2}{T_{g2}} \qquad (2)$$

The previous expression is useful for the calculation of the Tg of a mixture by knowing the weight fractions of each of the components and its respective Tg. From this expression it is possible to determine the compositions of the conjugated phases by arranging terms and making some assumptions:

$$w_2' = \frac{T_{g2} \cdot (T_{g1} - T_g')}{T_g' \cdot (T_{g1} - T_{g2})} \qquad (3)$$

$$w_1'' = \frac{T_{g1} \cdot (T_g'' - T_2)}{T_g'' \cdot (T_{g1} - T_{g2})} \qquad (4)$$

where: w: Weight fraction

1 Subindex referred to PC

2 Subindex referred to SAN

' Superindex referred to conjugated phase rich in PC

'' Superindex referred to conjugated phase rich in SAN

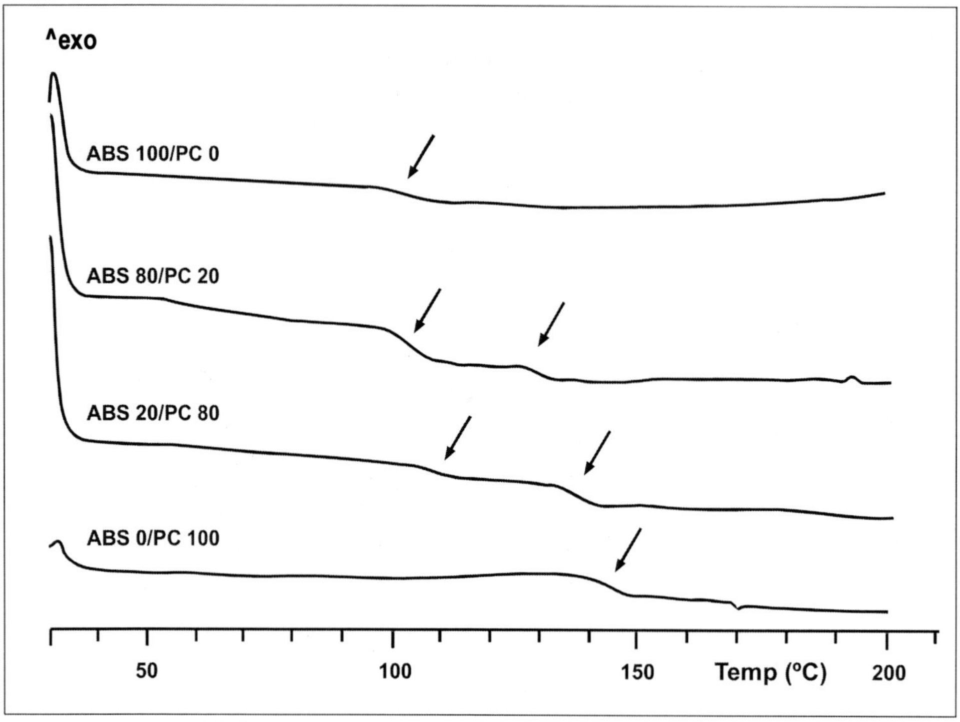

Figure 5. DSC curves of different blends of ABS/PC system.

Results corresponding to the compositions of conjugated phases of ABS and PC calculated according to the Tg of each one of these phases is summarized in Table 2. It can be observed a bigger solubility in polycarbonate than in ABS. Although the solubility of the components is not total, it is enough for the establishment of some interaction that confers good properties to the blends.

Table 2. Weight Fractions of Conjugated Phases, Resulting from Blends of ABS and PC

% w ABS	PC rich phase		SAN rich phase	
	w'$_1$	w'$_2$	w"$_1$	w"$_2$
100	—	—	—	—
90	0,4954	0,5046	0,0045	0,9955
80	0,5729	0,4271	0,0048	0,9952
70	0,6404	0,3596	0,0630	0,9370
60	0,6637	0,3363	0,0093	0,9907
40	0,7632	0,2368	0,0727	0,9273
30	0,7983	0,2017	0,1451	0,8549
20	0,8927	0,1073	0,1750	0,8250
10	0,9948	0,0052	0,2093	0,7907
0	—	—	—	—

PREPARATION OF BLENDS FROM RECYCLED ENGINEERING PLASTICS

Preparation of blends has been carried out by means of an extruder. Previously, and because of the avidity of both materials for moisture, they have been dried off for 12 h. at a temperature of 60-65 ºC, paying special attention to polycarbonate to avoid hydrolysis processes at medium-high temperatures. Temperatures in extrusion process have varied in the range of 220 ºC for blends with high content in ABS up to 290 ºC for blends with high contents in polycarbonate.

Blends with most interest are those which are processed with similar conditions to ABS (polycarbonate content around 15-20 % by weight). All the other blends find more difficulties in the extrusion process and they need higher processing temperatures which can be responsible of degradation processes on the elastomeric phase (polybutadiene) dispersed in the SAN matrix of ABS.

The previous degradation level that accumulate both materials produce a decrease on the polymeric chains length that affect to mechanical and thermal performance of ABS/PC and processability of the system. The small molecular weight species resulting from degradation processes, basically coming from ABS, exercise a plasticization effect that improves the processability of blends. In this sense, the excellent processability of these blends with ABS and PC (with small amount of polycarbonate) is a decisive characteristic in order to carry out recycling of these materials since they show a good balance of mechanical and thermal properties. Characterization of the melt can be carried out by means of rheometry techniques such the determination of the melt flow index (MFI) and the viscosimetric techniques. The results obtained on MFI for different residence times inside the cylinder heater (Figure 6) show a decrease on the viscosity as a consequence of thermo-oxidative processes, and basically it is ABS the one that suffers bigger variation of MFI because of degradation of polybutadiene since its structure is more susceptible to oxidation due to the presence of double bonds with tertiary hydrogens easy to extract by the oxygen action. This situation drives to formation of oxidized species, basically hydroxyl and carbonyl groups [9].

These thermal oxidation processes in ABS cause a partial reduction of the polybutadiene grafting to SAN matrix. Although this situation makes processing easier, also generate many zones with lack of adherence with the SAN matrix, acting as stress concentrators (Figure 7) and they can cause premature fracture. This lack of adherence will be the responsible of the decrease on impact strength of blends with different compositions.

The results show an increment of the flow with the addition of polycarbonate. This phenomenon is a decisive factor to recycle these materials. Polycarbonate is more viscous than ABS, but blends with small amounts of PC are easily processed. This is due to a plasticization effect of polycarbonate. Blends with small amounts of PC can be processed at similar temperatures to those of ABS; higher amounts of PC implies higher ranges of processing (around 280-320 ºC) which can induce degradation processes on ABS.

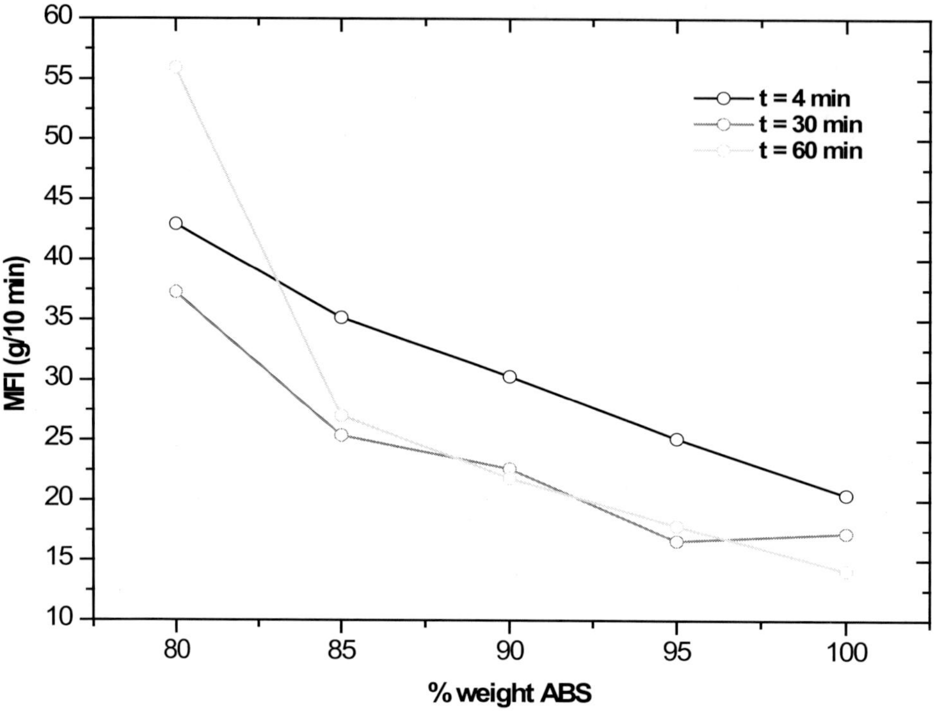

Figure 6. Variation of MFI for different blends of ABS/PC system at 230 °C and different residence times in the cylinder heater.

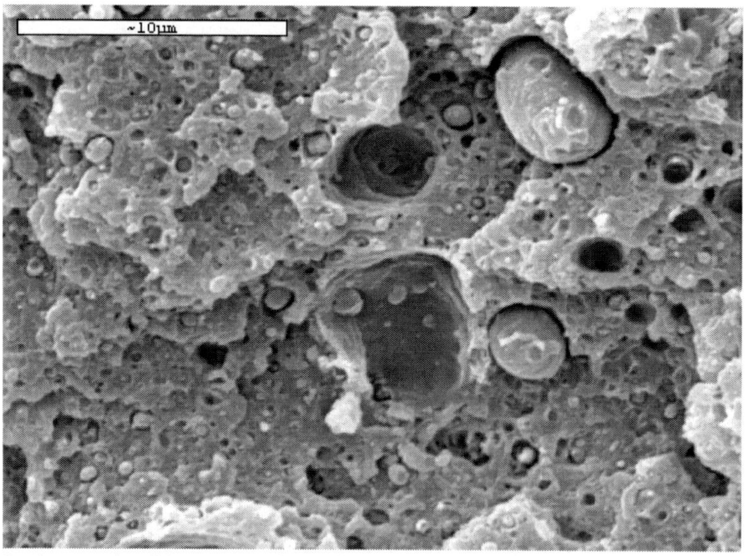

Figure 7. SEM micrograph of fracture surface of recycled ABS (x5000).

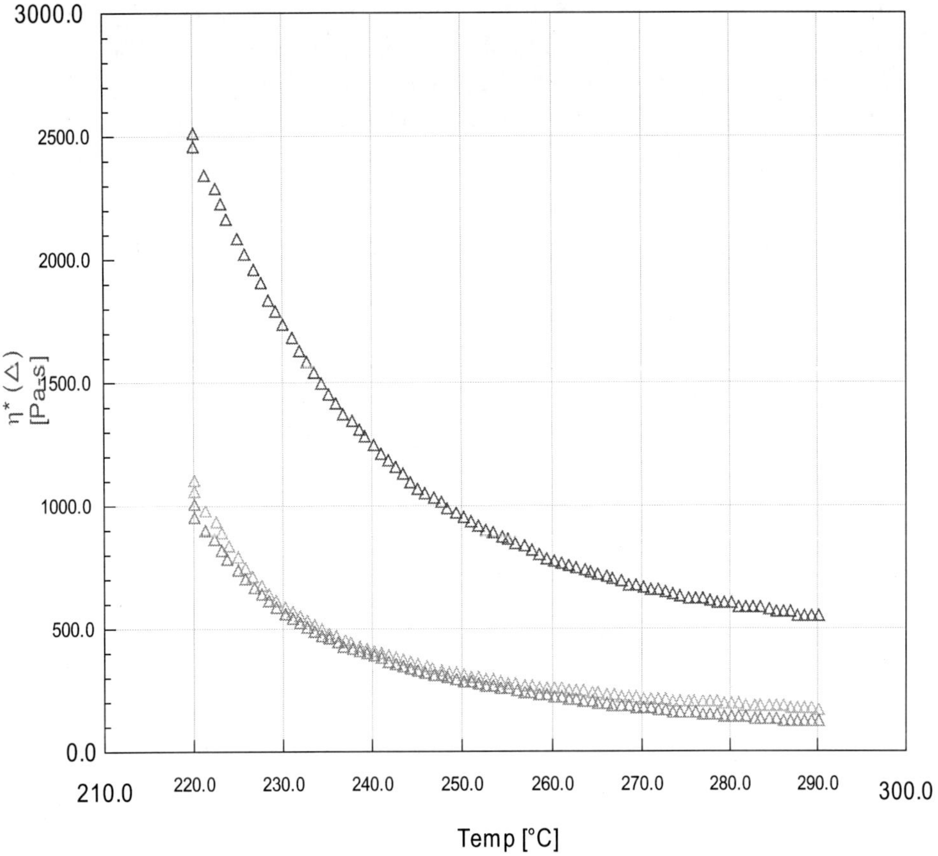

Figure 8. Variation of the viscosity with temperature for different blends of the ABS/PC system [% in weight].
(Δ recycledABS, Δ ABS 80 /PC 20, Δ ABS 40/PC 60).

Regarding the study by means of viscosimetry, results obtained with a plate-plate rheometer are similar to those observed on MFI (Figure 8). As it can be expected, the addition of polycarbonate performs an important decrease on the blend viscosity, so we can conclude that addition of polycarbonate improves processing conditions considerably. This behaviour is quite frequent in recycled materials blends, favouring its processability. The plasticization effect can be attributed to different processes:

- Plasticization due to the lack of miscibility of the components [10] which contributes to a chain orientation during the injection process. This plasticization is also due to the absence of interaction forces between both components and then, an internal plasticization effect takes place.
- Other phenomenon that takes part in the decrease on viscosity is attributable to the ABS degradation as a consequence of thermo-oxidative processes as described before. This degradation does not affect greatly to the global performance of the

blends, but it influences in a decisive way the viscosity of the blends, reducing the chain length and generating free radicals that can accelerate polycarbonate degradation. In any way, low molecular weight species present in ABS enter among polycarbonate chains and perform a reduction of the interaction forces, enabling free movement of these and, in consequence, reducing the viscosity due to internal friction between chains.

Mechanical Behaviour of the Blends with Partial Miscibility

One of the most influencing phenomena on the final performance of blends is the miscibility of components. A high miscibility is consequence of an excellent interaction between components, and this contributes to good mechanical properties. The absence of miscibility or even a partial miscibility implies the absence of interaction between components and this is the cause of a reduction on mechanical properties. Previous degradation processes can also influence in an important way on mechanical performance of blends.

Preparation of blends is an interesting possibility to improve performance of materials. ABS is a fragile polymer (Figure 9); its impact resistance can be improved with the addition of some component of ductile nature such as polycarbonate (Figure 10). Polycarbonate is a material of high toughness and in fact, many commercial blends of virgin materials are based on the excellent combination of properties of ABS and PC.

Nevertheless, mechanical properties of blends coming from recycled materials are affected by the nature and level of previous degradation of wastes. ABS/PC is a partial miscibility system as seen before and this will contribute to a system with phase separation. The limited interaction between different phases is responsible of the reduction on mechanical properties of this system. The most sensitive properties to partial miscibility are ductile properties such as impact strength, elongation at break and toughness, since in these properties, the phenomena of stress concentration due to the presence of different phases act in a decisive way.

Considering the nature of the materials (wastes) with partial miscibility is not expectable to obtain optimal properties, even without the use of any compatibilizer agent in order to improve interphase interaction. The objective of the study on mechanical performance of these mixtures is to know which is the range of compositions which shows good balance of properties, impact behaviour and in general ductile properties, since in the case of blends with low miscibility, these are the most critical properties (Figures 11 and 12).

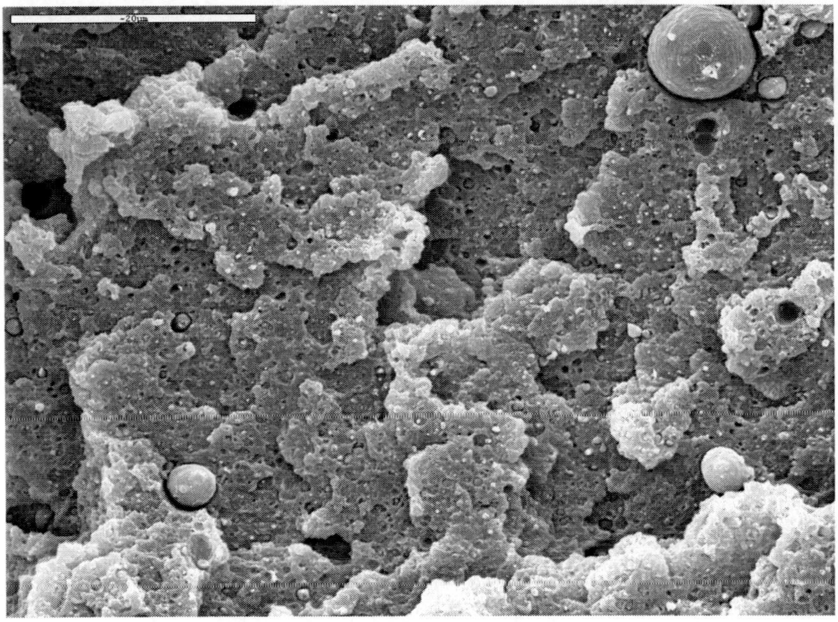

Figure 9. SEM micrograph of a sample of recycled ABS, x2000.

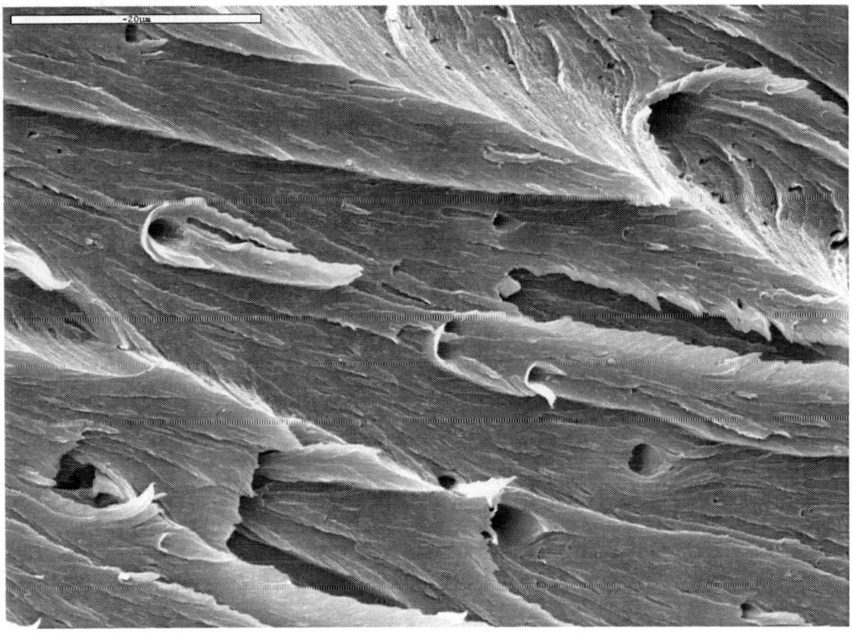

Figure 10. SEM micrograph of a sample of recycled PC, x2000.

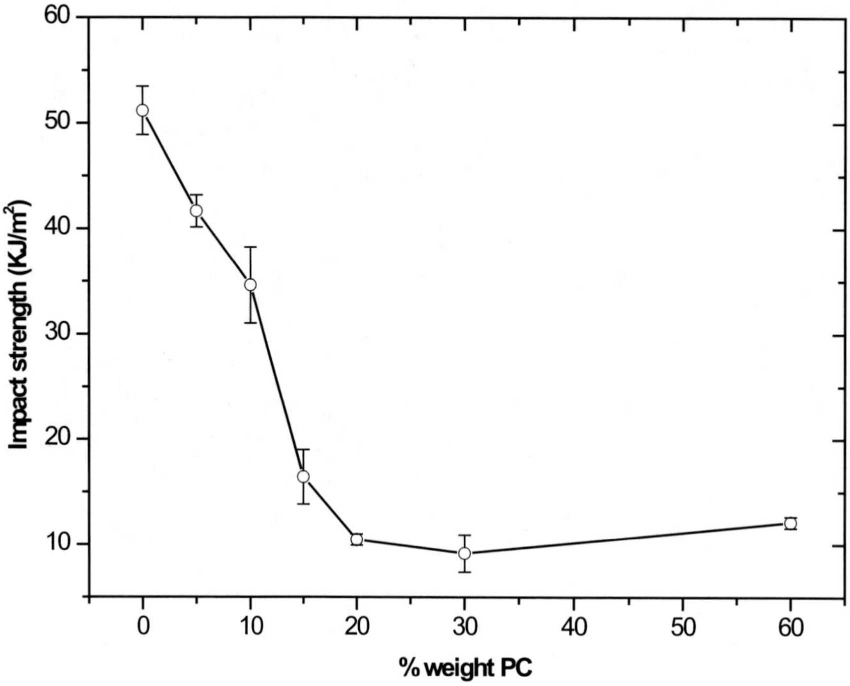

Figures 11. Variation of impact energy as a function of % by weight of PC for ABS/PC system

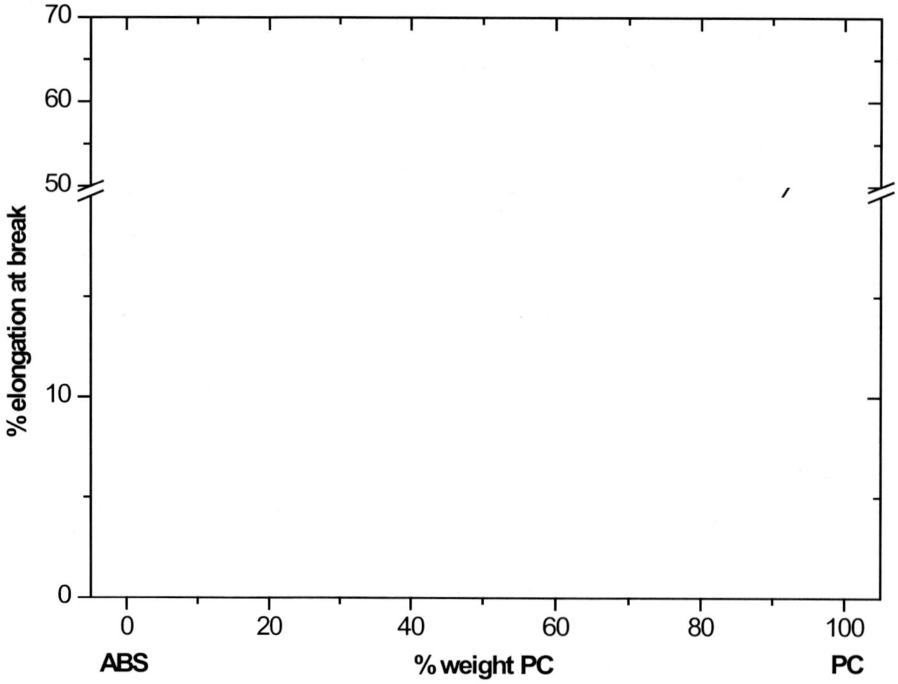

Figure 12. Variation of the % elongation at break (% A) as a function of % by weight of PC for ABS/PC system

This reduction on impact energy for intermediate compositions is typical of blends with partial miscibility due to the low interaction between the different phases that form these blends. As they are recycled materials, this fact is accentuated due to the previous degradation level accumulated by both components. In these cases, the study of the impact behaviour of the system shows the need to incorporate some component to improve it.

Intermediate compositions are the most sensitive to the existence of low phase interaction among the different components of the system. These compositions show co-continuity behaviour and the performances of the system is defined by both materials. In this area, the lack of adherence intervenes in a decisive way in a deterioration of mechanical resistance as consequence of the stress concentration in the interphase. One of the interesting fields could be the development of compatibilizer agents or impact modifiers which allow to improve the performance of the system in intermediate compositions.

The incorporation of compatibilizers agents can improve ductile properties considerably maintaining practically in the same level resistant properties. This is due to the improvement in the interaction among the PC rich phase and SAN rich phase such as shown in Figure 13.

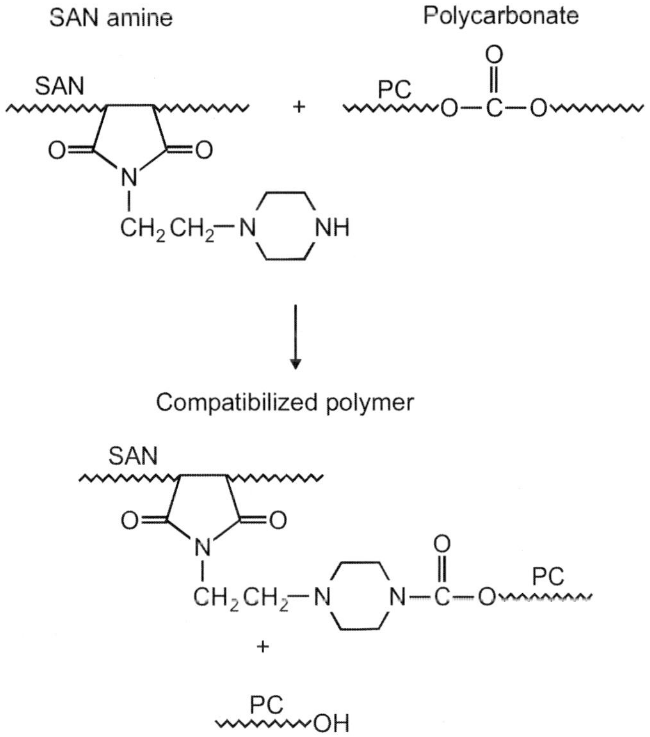

Figures 13. Scheme of possible compatibilization of ABS/PC blends.

CONCLUSIONS

Recycling of engineering plastics finds some problems due to the low volume of wastes generated in comparison to commodities and the difficulty of processing that generally demands more complex equipment than conventional ones. ABS and PC are widely used in electrical and electronics equipment industry and the amount of wastes is considerable.

Preparation of ABS/PC blends from these wastes is an interesting possibility to undertake recycling processes.

As they are recycled materials, it is important to know and quantify the previous level of degradation. ABS is susceptible of thermal degradation because of the presence of double bonds in butadiene phase dispersed in a SAN matrix. PC shows great thermal and light resistance but it can suffer from hydrolysis in contact with moisture as all polyesters. These degradation processes results in a decrease on chain length which contributes to a plasticization effect which improves processability, but some performances are considerably reduced, such as impact strength, % elongation at break, and, generally, all ductile properties. The addition of compatibilizer agents can be an interesting field in order to improve this behaviour which is due to a low interaction between the different phases that form the blend because the absence of total miscibility.

Preparation of blends with ABS and PC in composition near to their generation ratio (4 to 1 for ABS and PC respectively) is highly interesting because it permits PC recycling which could not be possible in an individual way due to its low volume generation if compared with ABS or commodities.

ACKNOWLEDGEMENTS

The authors thank "Ministerio de Ciencia y Tecnología", Ref: MAT2003-05511 for the financial support. Special thanks are given to Mr. Jorge Ramis and Mr. Francisco Pérez from ACTECO for the technical support on this work.

REFERENCES

[1] Casale, A. and Salvatore, O., *Polymer Engineering and Science*, *15:8,* 286-293 (1975).

[2] Kim, J.K., Polym.-plast. *Technol. Eng.*, *34:11*, 875-890 (1996).

[3] Paul, D.R. and Bucknall, C.B. (Eds.), *Polymer Blends*, Willey-Interscience, New York, 1999.

[4] Tiganis, B.E., Burn, L.S., Davis, P. and Hill, A.J., *Polymer Degradation and Stability*, *76:10*, 425 -434 (2002).

[5] Rivaton, A., Mailhot, B., Soulestin, J., Varghese, H. and Gardette, J.L., *Polymer Degradation and Stability*, *75:17*, 17-33 (2002).

[6] McNeill, I.C. and Rincon, A., *Polymer Degradation and Stability*, *39:7*, 13-19 (1993).

[7] Kolarik, J., and Lednicky, F., *Polymer Engineering and Science*, *37:10*, 128-137 (1997).

[8] Markgraf, K. and Abetz, V., *e-Polymers*, *15*, (2001).

[9] Boldizar, A. and Möller, K., *Polymer Degradation and Stability*, *81:8*, 359-366 (2003).

[10] Seo, Y. and Kim, H.J., *Polymer Engineering and Science, 42:10*, 951-960 (2002).

In: New Developments in Polymer Analysis, Stabilization... ISBN 1-59454-511-1
Editors: G.E. Zaikov and A. Jiménez, pp. 101-114

Chapter 8

AGING OF POLYESTER MATRIX IN SALINE WATER

L. Sanchez,* D. García, R. Balart and F. Parres

Department of Mechanical and Materials Engineering. Polytechnic University of Valencia. Paseo Viaducto, 1 03801 Alcoy (Spain). e-mail: lsanchez@mcm.upv.es

ABSTRACT

The behaviour of unsaturated polyester resins with marine environment at room temperature is evaluated to determine the degradation in the mechanical properties of the material. On the other hand, the cured state of a thermosetting resin is an important characteristic. The cured state is calculated as the fraction of heat in the reaction. The correlation between the amount of water absorbed at room temperature, the values of cured state and the degradation on mechanical properties are developed in this work. The following parameters were measured during the test: change of weight, ultimate tensile strength, tensile modulus, hardness, elongation at break, impact strength. The measurement was performed during 500 hours with the resin immersed in saline water (35% NaCl), simulating marine environment, for different cured state and with cured resin at different temperatures.

Key words: Polyester; Degradation; Aging; Crosslinking, Diffusion.

INTRODUCTION

Polyesters are the most widely used thermoset resins. Polyester resins are often used in marine applications, nautical construction and other naval products. One obstacle that is breaking the success of the polymeric matrix materials in civil engineering applications is the susceptibility that presents the polymeric matrix in front of the degradation due to moisture, temperature and corrosive chemical atmospheres in general. At the moment the problem

* Corresponding author.

produced by the service environment in infrastructures is one of the main reasons in the development and use of advanced materials, as the reinforced polymers, in naval engineering applications. Because of its high specific strength, low weight, fatigue and corrosion resistance, these materials are good for structural uses in this field.

At the present time there are very few studies about the effect of the moisture, saline and alkaline environments at long term in the typical polymers in these applications. It is necessary to analyze the polymeric degradation mechanisms to optimize the use of the suitable materials, production and processing and applications [1,2].

Polymeric materials generally absorb moisture in appraisable grades when they are immersed directly in water or when they are exposed to wet atmospheres. The quantity of moisture absorbed depends on the chemical nature of the material, so the water absorption speed for the plastics follows defined mathematical models. This absorption is characterized to have reversible and irreversible effects on the properties and processing of the material. The absorbed moisture has demonstrated to act as polymer plasticizer, decreasing the glass transition temperature (Tg) and their strength properties, although these effects can be reversible. The absorbed water also induces a physical corrosion, or irreversible mechanic damaged, cause of the microcrack formation or cracks together with a high chemical degradation in the polymer structure.

The mechanisms that induce the breaking caused by moisture absorption in the unsaturated polyester resins are quite complex. Some authors have demonstrated that the action of water in these resins is a combination of the leaching of components with lower molecular mass initially present in the resin, the chemical attack on the ester bond, and the plasticization cause by the absorbed water. Other authors base their study on the effect caused by the hydrolysis as irreversible process, accelerated by the microcracks appearance in the material [3].

Also, a great percentage of the applications in unsaturated polyester resins use manual lamination techniques, and the post-cured conditions are not adequate, so materials with structures not completely crosslinking are produced. These structures can be more easily attacked by a liquid in contact with them. Most of the processes for obtaining resin pieces of unsaturated polyester are carried out at room temperature, so total curing of the resin is not reached, due to the inhibition of the cured process. As a result, the material presents lower thermal stability, low hydrolysis resistance and shows more inflation problems in contact with solvents because the cure was not complete [4,5].

The exposure of polyester resin with different state of cure in saline water induces degradation in the mechanical properties and the morphology of the resin specimens. Incomplete crosslinking induces low resistance to hydrolysis and greater degradation on mechanical properties. The study of the degradation mechanism should consider chemical and physical aspects.

KINETICS OF ABSORPTION OF SALINE WATER

Following these guidelines, we think about the study of the degradation kinetics of the unsaturated polyester resin in saline environment for different cured states by mean of a series of different crosslinking grades, obtained for different cured temperatures, both in cured as post-cured state. All tests were planned by duplicate; one series stays in the air at room temperature as reference, and the other one in a saline environment at room temperature. With this position we wanted to analyze the effect of the marine degradation kinetics in a standard polyester resin.

Since we intended to evaluate the behaviour of unsaturated polyester resin in saline water at room temperature by means of water absorption kinetics, two parameters were quantified as characteristic of these kinetic: the amount of absorbed water and the diffusivity. The best way for determining the behaviour of a resin immersed in a liquid is to analyze the absorption kinetics by means of the material weight increase regarding time [6]. The weight increase is represented in terms of weight change percentage as:

$$M = \frac{Weight_{sample} - Weight_{dry-sample}}{Weight_{dry-sample}} \tag{1}$$

In cured state the resin presents a higher absorption capacity than in post-cured state. Although the difference is low, it is observed that the crosslinking state of the material or, what is the same, the internal structure of the polymer, is fundamental regarding the polymer behaviour in front of the absorption in a liquid environment, presenting better behaviour in post-cured state. Therefore, the crosslinking state of the resin is a fundamental parameter in the quantification and pursuit of the saline water absorption kinetics in this kind of resins.

A completely parallel behaviour was observed for the different cured grades, with very similar values. It is necessary to feature the slight increase in the absorption water capacity corresponding to low crosslinking grades.

Incomplete polymerization, as well as a great number of bond ester presence, cause in the resin a lower thermal stability, lower hydrolysis resistance and higher inflation grade in the solvent than in resins that present a complete cured state. The ester group hydrolysis cause the formation of carboxyl groups that show an autocatalytic decomposition. The study of the degradation mechanisms keeps in mind both physical and chemical aspects. Unsaturated polyester resins suffer a slow degradation process when they suffer aging due to the water molecules absorption [7].

The mass coefficient transferred on the surface of the tested samples is very high and the tangent of the curves represented in the Figure 1 at the beginning of the test is very vertical. This absorption kinetics follows a "Fickian" diffusion process, so it follows the Fick laws, with a constant diffusivity. Initially the curves present a linear behaviour, and later a typical Fick concave zone. When the absorption conditions follow the Fick laws, the weight variations are calculated by:

$$M = \left\{ 1 - \frac{8}{\pi^2} \sum_{j=0}^{\infty} \frac{\exp\left[(-2j+1)^2 \pi^2 \left(Dt/h^2 \right) \right]}{(2j+1)^2} \right\} (Mm - Mi) + Mi \tag{2}$$

where *Mi*: initial moisture content (0); *Mm*: maximum moisture content; *h*:sample thickness; *t*: time;*D*: diffusivity constant for each sample.

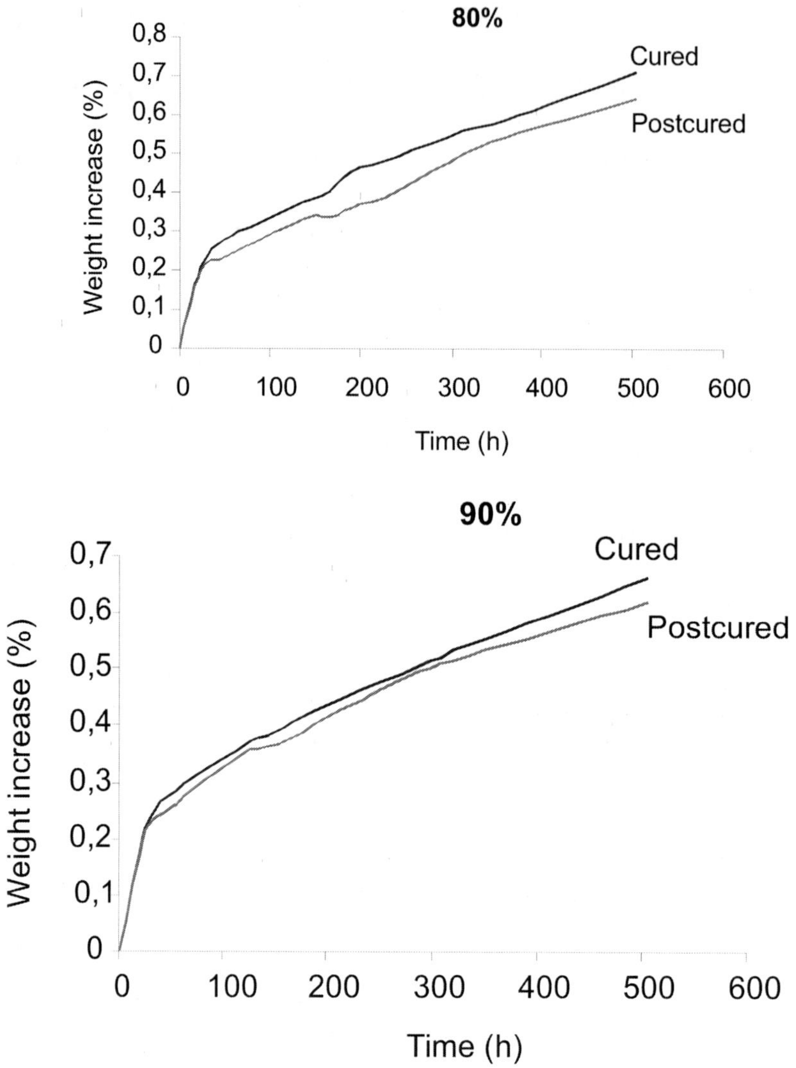

Figure 1. Saline water absorption kinetics for different crosslinking grades (80% and 90%) in cured state and post-cured state. (cured at 60ºC).

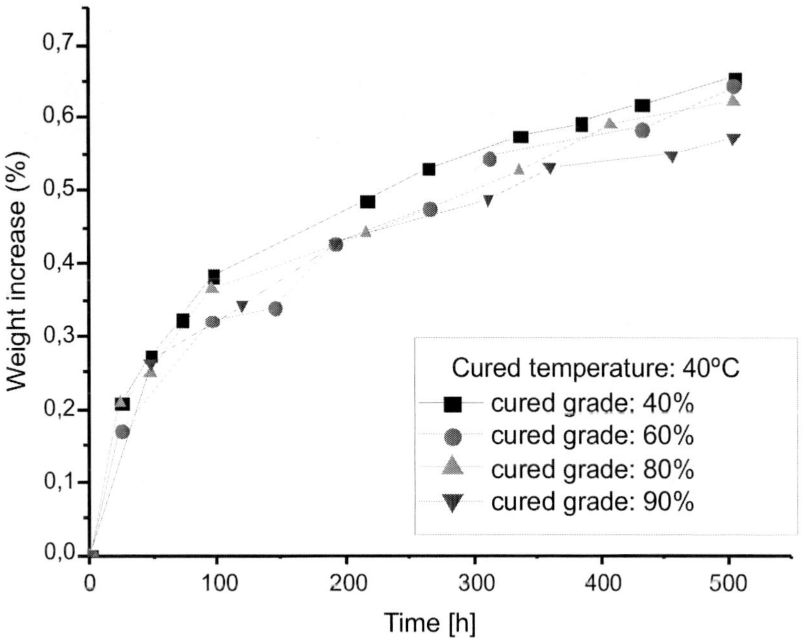

Figure 2. Saline water absorption kinetics in post-cured state.

As it has been observed, in Fickian diffusion, the absorption kinetics is characterized by two fundamental parameters: the diffusivity and the quantity of absorbed water [6,8,9]. In many cases, the calculated and the experimental value coincide reasonably well until the maximum weight corresponding to the saturation is reached. Beyond this point, the data usually differ to the calculated values, the differences between the average and the calculated values are more marked for the test made at high temperatures. Some studies have demonstrated that the aging for water absorption in polymers at high temperature can cause damage in way of cracks, microcracks and other types of morphological changes allowing an additional absorption.

The relative weight increase is represented vs. the square root of immersion time to obtain experimentally the diffusion coefficient. The curve presents a positive deviation of the moisture content at balance reached in a first stage.

For the determination of constant D, by means of Fick law diffusion application, the following equation is used:

$$D = \pi\left(\frac{h}{4 \cdot Mm}\right)^2 \left(\frac{M_2 - M_1}{\sqrt{t_2} - \sqrt{t_1}}\right)^2 \left(1 + \frac{h}{l} + \frac{h}{n}\right)^{-2} \quad (3)$$

where, l: sample length; n: sample width; M_1 *and* M_2: moisture contents for times t_1 and t_2, these times should be low enough to maintain a lineal variation with the time.

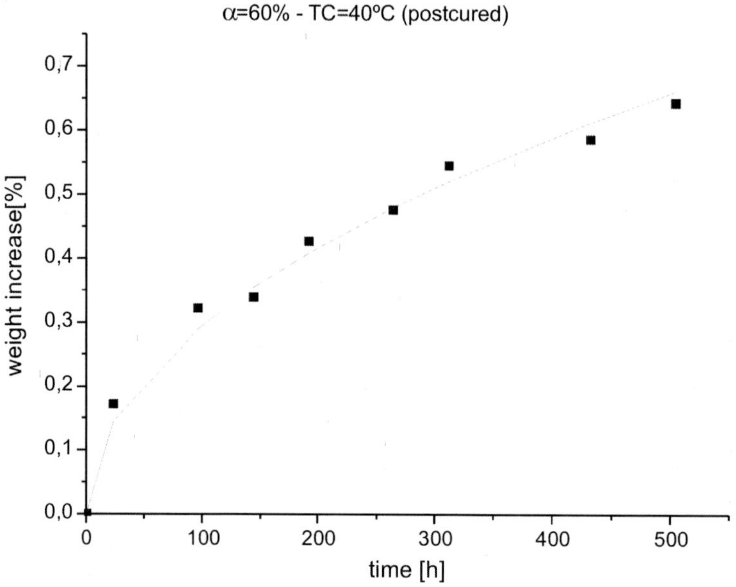

Figure 3. Weight increase in saline environment versus time.

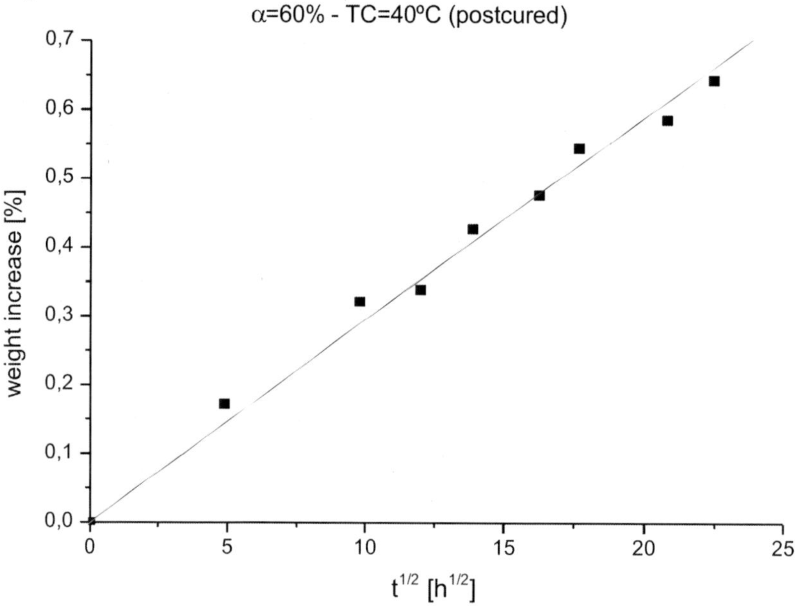

Figure 4. Weight increase in saline environment as a function of $t^{1/2}$

When representing the diffusivity coefficient and the weight increase vs. the crosslinking grade, a marked parallelism is observed in both parameters in front of the internal structure state of the material determined by the crosslinking grade. Figure 5 demonstrates how the diffusivity coefficient and the weight increase by immersion in water saline are bigger for low crosslinking grades than for high crosslinking grades.

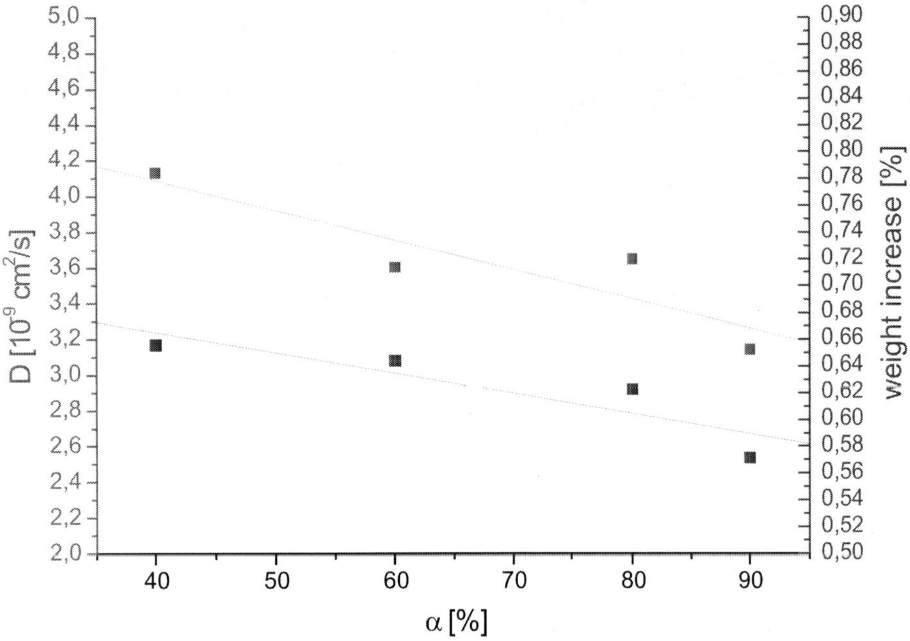

Figure 5. Correlation among crosslinking state, weight increase and diffusivity coefficient. (curing temperature: 40°C)

Aging Effects

The obtained results demonstrate that the mechanical properties of the material suffer a remarkable decrease caused by the water absorption effect, that is to say, caused by the resin degradation in a saline environment, both in cured as post-cured state. From the obtained experimental data, it is necessary to keep in mind that due to the fragile nature of the material, the elongation values obtained are very low and they do not contribute to obtain specific information. In the same way, the impact strength values obtained are extremely low, there is not a high difference among values obtained for different curing grades, although it can be observed a slight embrittlement of the resin in the degraded state when absorbing less energy in their break for impact.

On the other hand, the quantification of mechanical behaviour in front of traction tensile allows to compare those values obtained for the tensile strength, as a valid parameter for the quantification of the material degradation in saline water immersion, as shown in figure 6 and 7. And since hardness is also a resistant mechanical characteristic, it presents a parallel behaviour to the tensile strength.

The exposure of resins in water produces modifications in the mechanical properties and in samples morphology. Also, the loss of low molecular mass components initially present in the resin, play an important paper as embrittlement causes. The chemical attack on the ester bond can be the responsible of the low strength that presents the material after being degraded in water environment. The degradation mechanism can be associated to the low chemical resistance and to the possible migration of some components initially present in the resin [7].

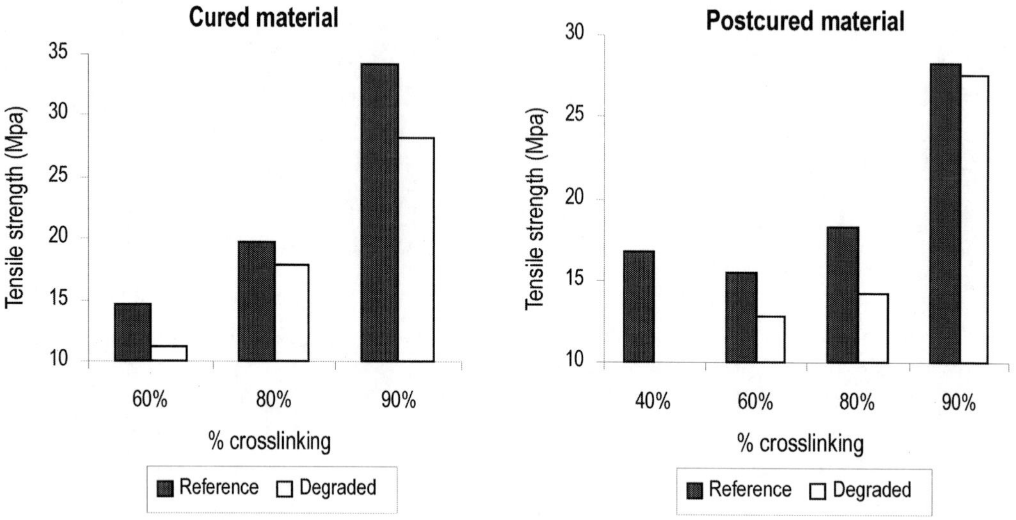

Figure 6. Tensile strength variation caused by the degradation effect, for different crosslinking grades of resin, in cured and post-cured state. (cure temperature 60ºC)

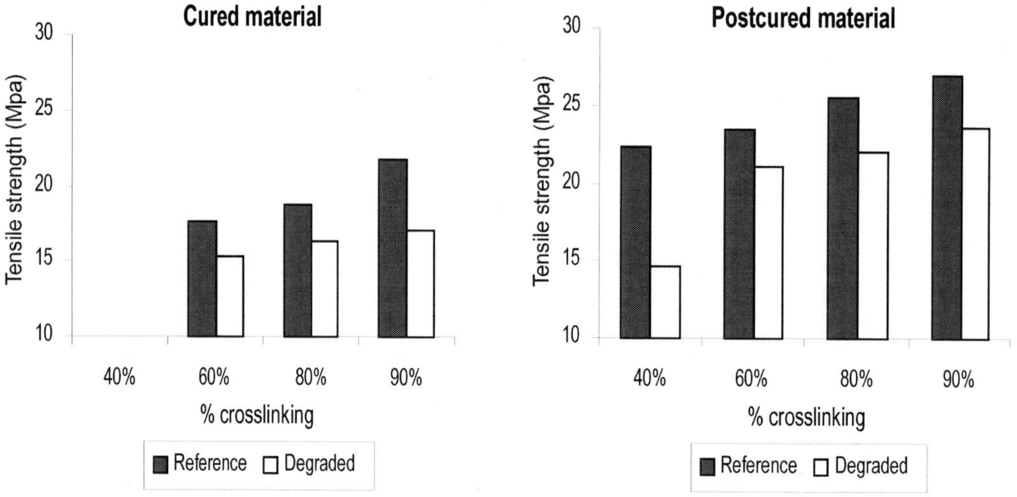

Figure 7. Tensile strength variation caused by the degradation effect, for different crosslinking grades of resin, in cured and post-cured state. (cure temperature 40ºC)

The moisture absorption acts as a plasticizer and as agent promoter of the hydrolysis, decreasing the mechanical properties of the resin that depend on temperature to which the material has been exposed. However, while the plasticization is a reversible phenomenon that disappears after a drying, the chemical degradation is irreversible. The material embrittlement is the result of the segments desegregations that causes the non-aged resin flexibility. [7]

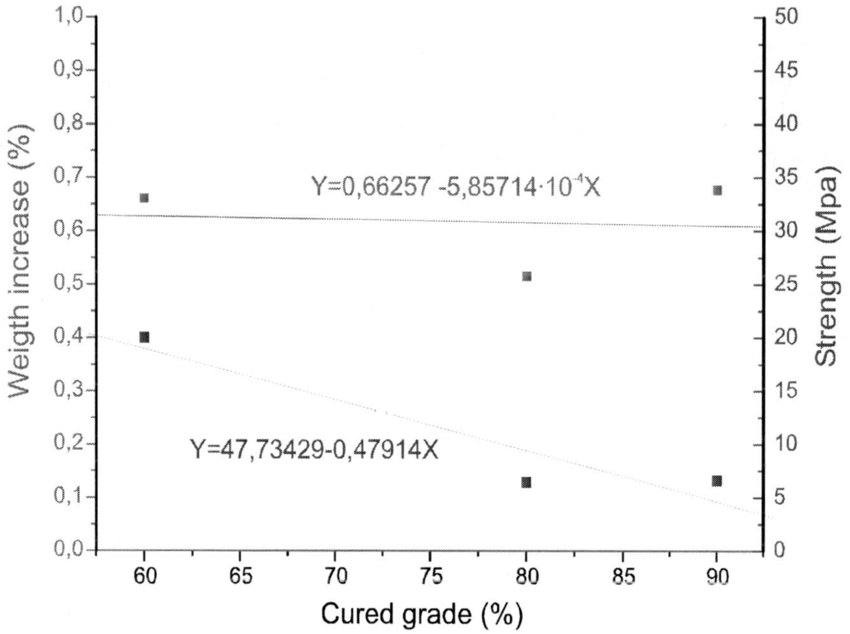

Figure 8. Correlation between the crosslinking state, weight increase and relative loss of strength. (cure temperature 40°C).

There is not a clear correlation between the loss of strength in the aged material and the weight change suffered, therefore it cannot be settled down the relationship between the weight change and the mechanical properties change in the resin. [8]

MORPHOLOGY OF SURFACES FRACTURES

The morphology of the typically fragile break surfaces of unsaturated polyester resin is characterized by two aspects: mirror and hackle. The rough aspect of the breaking surface of the samples belongs to a fragile fracture of the resin with hackle surface morphology. The smooth aspect corresponds to the mirror region.

It is necessary to feature how this mirror zone appears more or less centered and surrounded of hackle surface with high roughness. The breaking process in the material will begin on some superficial defect of samples giving place to the crack apparition that grows toward interior, reducing the section without damage of the material. In this cracks small microfissures that grow up by the effect of the applied stress appear. The advance course of microfissures is highly convergent toward a central point, easily visible.

When comparing the surface morphologies in degraded state and in reference state, differences are not observed, what means that the mechanisms causing the material fracture are the same: microfissures nucleation, growth and crack formation. The absorption process of saline water developed by an experimental way does not influence the mechanisms that cause the material breaking when it is subjected to traction stress. This is demonstrated by the morphologies of the breaking surfaces after this test.

Nevertheless, it is interesting to feature how the physical aspect of samples suffers a remarkable change. The samples degraded in saline environment acquire a whitish aspect, losing the transparency and the shine that maintain the samples in reference state, that is to say, without degradation.

Although from the morphological aspect of the breaking surfaces, the crosslinking grade effect in the internal structure of the resin is not as outstanding as the mechanical properties quantification. With this analysis we can conclude that the material degradation is function of the cure grade, that is to say, of the internal structure of the polymer, and of the cure conditions. By low magnification (x150), the mirror zone of the fracture surface is characterized to present higher roughness in the degraded state. By high magnification it is observed how at aged state there are formation of very marked crack fronts that indicate a more violent breaking that corresponding to the reference state, with a more uniform aspect, and less voluminous cracks crests (x800). It is also interesting to observe the mechanism of microcracks or microfissures formation, as responsible of the material failure. These studies allow to corroborate the data obtained by the macroscopic analysis of samples.

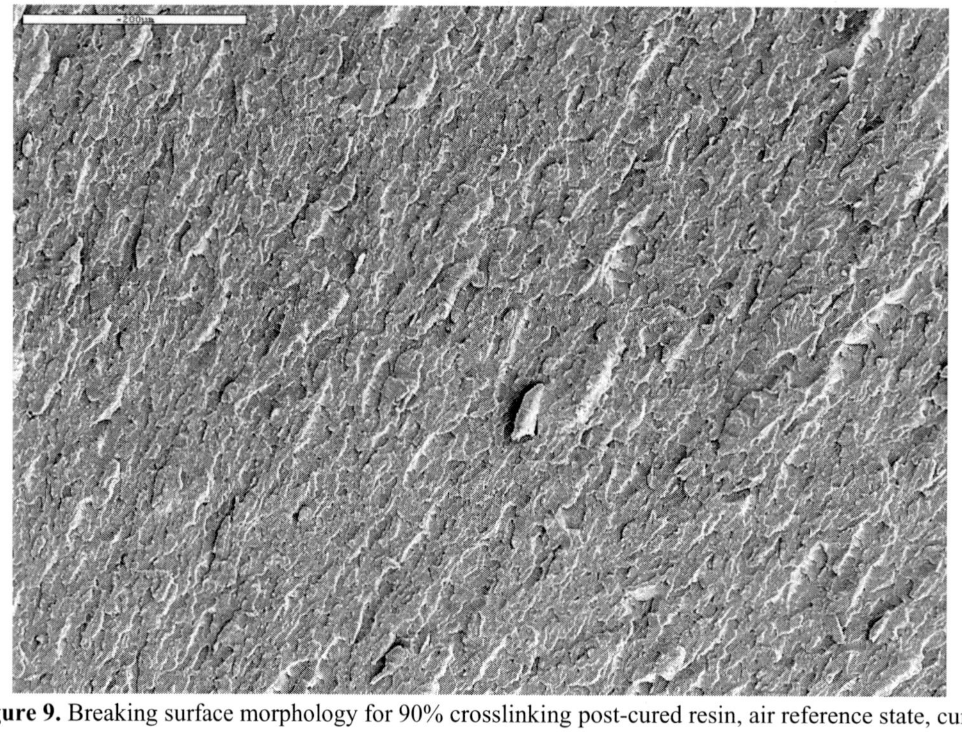

Figure 9. Breaking surface morphology for 90% crosslinking post-cured resin, air reference state, cure temperature 60ºC, mirror zone (x 150)

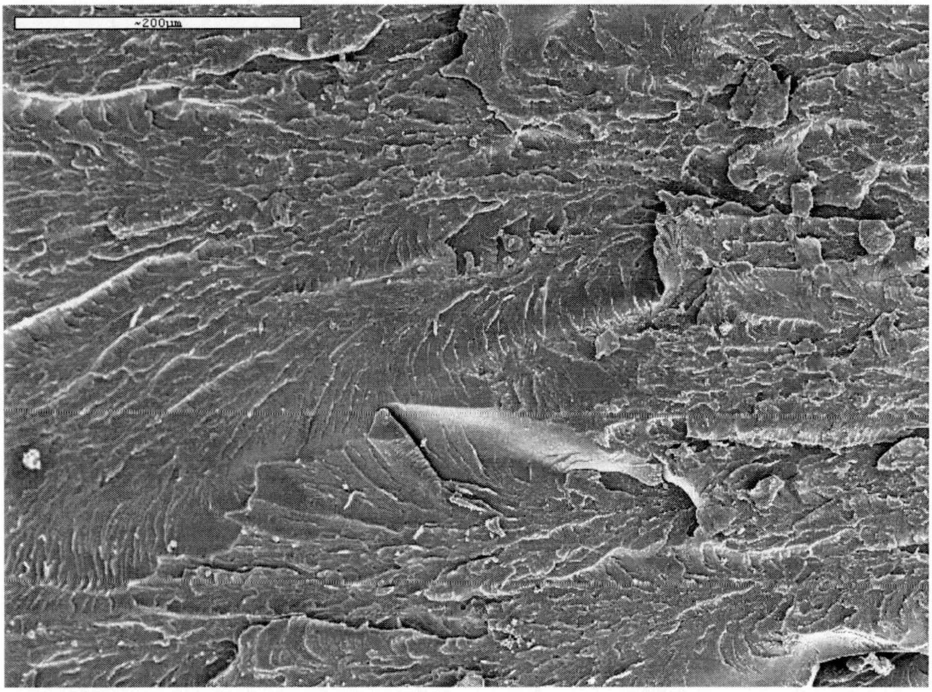

Figure 10. Breaking surface morphology for 90% crosslinking post-cured resin, water degradation state, cure temperature 60ºC, mirror zone (x 150)

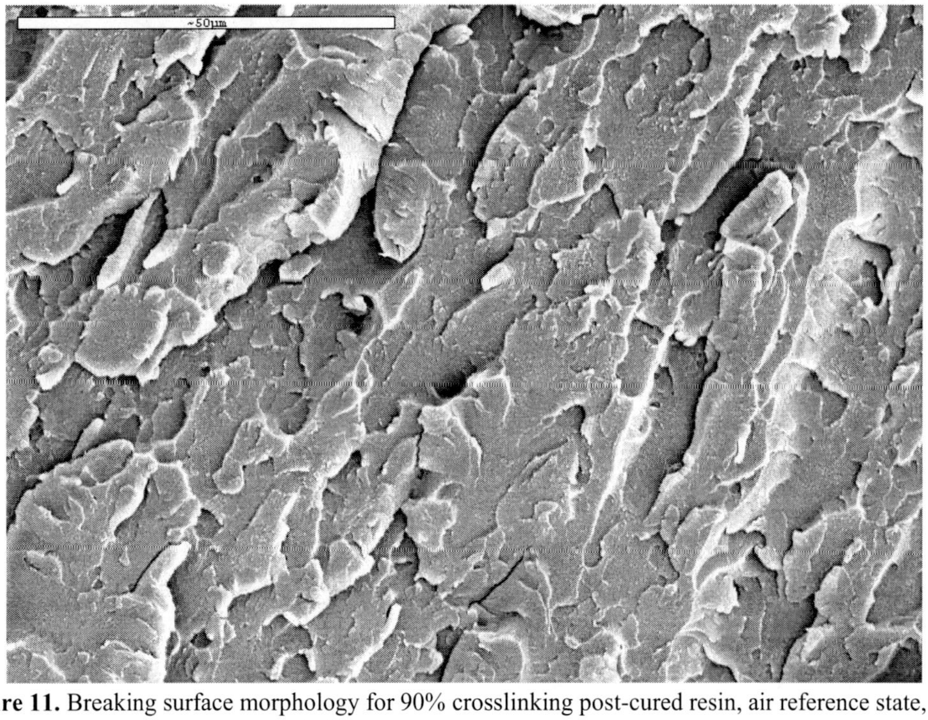

Figure 11. Breaking surface morphology for 90% crosslinking post-cured resin, air reference state, cure temperature 60ºC, mirror zone. (x 800)

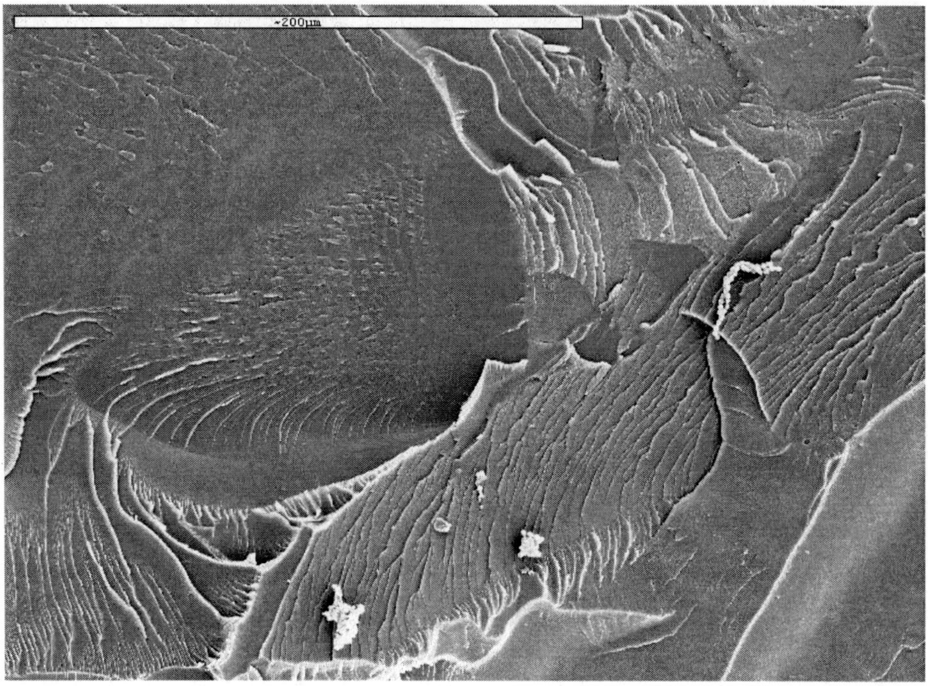

Figure 12. Breaking surface morphology for 90% crosslinking post-cured resin, water degradation state, cure temperature 60ºC, central zone. (x 300)

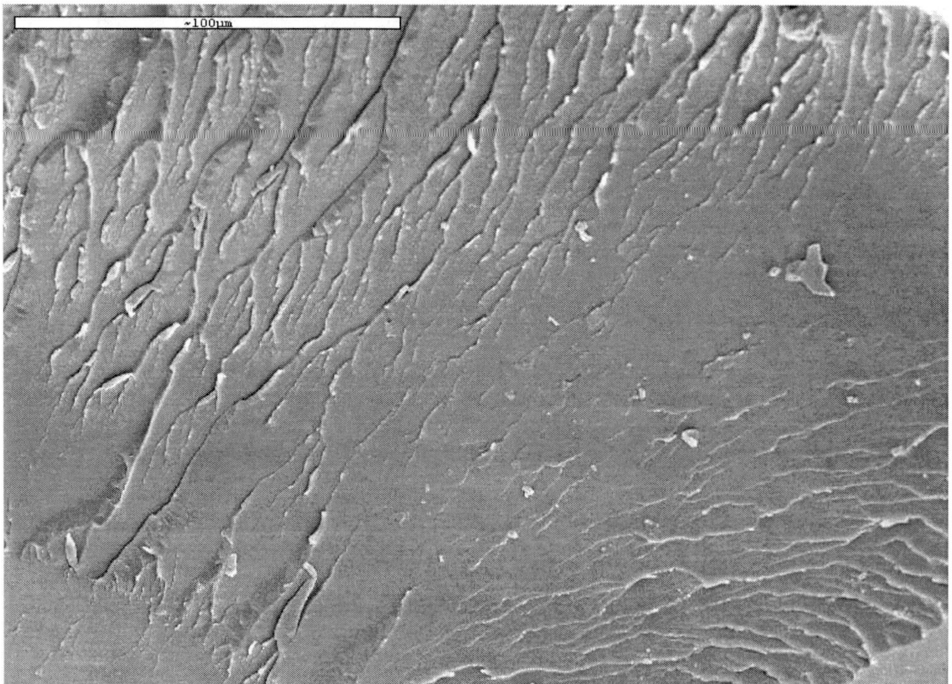

Figure 13. Microcracks formation detail, water degradation state. (x 400).

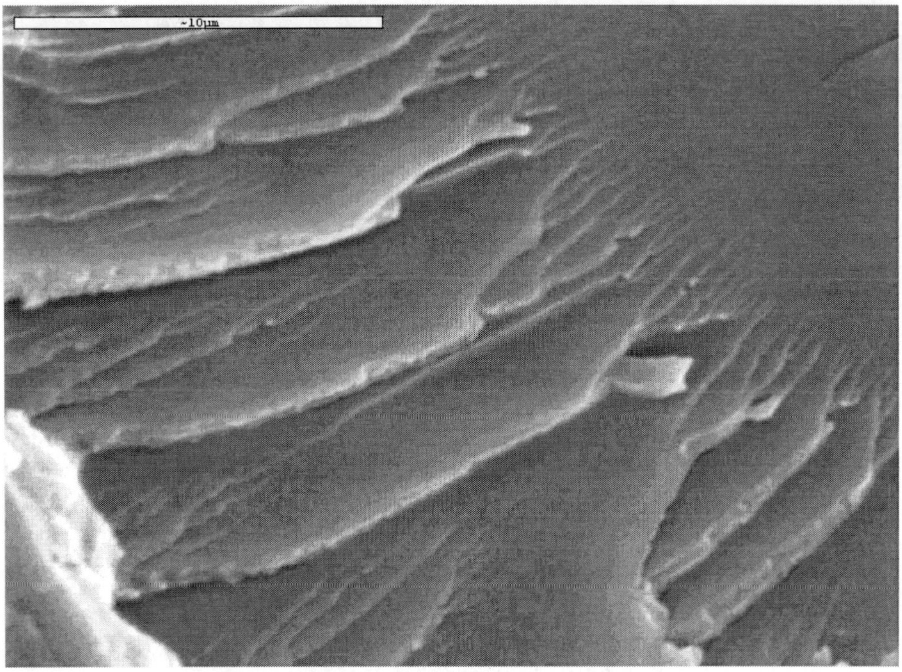

Figure 14. Microcracks formation detail, water degradation state. (x 4000)

CONCLUSIONS

The process of absorption of water is described by "Fickian" diffusion with constant diffusivity. The diffusivity decreases linearly with the value of the state of cure. The amount of water absorbed decreases linearly with the value of the cure state. An internal resin structure with high crosslinking grade presents lower water absorption capacity than a structure with low crosslinking grade. The resistant mechanical characteristics of the material suffer a remarkable decrease for the effect of absorption of water. The develop of absorption of water saline in an experimental way, does not influence the mechanism that cause the breaking of the material when it is subjected to traction loads. It is demonstrated by the morphologies of the breaking surfaces that take place after this test.

REFERENCES

[1] Chin, J.W., Aouadi, K., Haight, M.R., Hughes, W.L., *Polymer Composites*, *22:14* 282-296 (2001).

[2] Davies, P., Choqueuse, D., Mazeas, F., *Progress in Durability of Composite System*, Reifsnider & Cardon (1998).

[3] Allen, R.C., Bauer, R.S, *ASM International* (1998).

[4] Apicella, A., Migliaresi, C., Nicodemo, L., Nicolais, L., Iaccarino, L., Roccotelli, S., Composites, 406-410 (1982).

[5] Valea, A., Gonzalez, M.L., Mondragón, I., *Journal of Applied Polymer Science, 71:7* 21-28 (1999).
[6] Benameur, T., Granger, R., Vergnaud, J.M., *Polymer Testing, 14:9* 35-44 (1995).
[7] Apicella, A., Migliaresi, C., Nicodemo, L., Nicolais, L., Iaccarino, L., Roccotelli, S., Composites, *14:8* 387-395 (1983).
[8] Sanders B.A.,. Tung R.W, *J. Composite Materials*, 14:19 213-232 (1980).
[9] Riccieri, J.E., Hecker de Carvalho, L., Vazquez, A., *Polymer Composites*, *20:8*, 29-37 (1999).

In: New Developments in Polymer Analysis, Stabilization... ISBN 1-59454-511-1
Editors: G.E. Zaikov and A. Jiménez, pp. 115-131

Chapter 9

THERMAL OXIDATION OF SOME POLYSACCHARIDES INVESTIGATED BY CHEMILUMINESCENCE

L. Matisová-Rychlá, J. Rychlý, I. Lacík and G. Kogan
Polymer Institute, Institute of Chemistry, Centre of Excellence for Degradation of Biopolymers, Slovak Academy of Sciences, Dúbravská cesta 9, 842 36 Bratislava, Slovak Republic
I. Janigová, K. Csomorová, M. Lazár and M. Strlič
Department of Chemistry and Chemical Technology, University of Ljubljana, Aškerčeva 5, Ljubljana, SI-1000, Slovenia
J. Kolar
National and University Library, Turjaška 1, Ljubljana, SI-1000, Slovenia

ABSTRACT

Thermal oxidation of the series of different polysaccharides based mainly on glucopyranose monomer unit (cellulose and its derivatives, mannan, chitin-glucan complex, etc.) have been studied by chemiluminescence analysis (CL) at the programmed heating of a sample in the temperature range 40 – 220 °C. The effect of substitution of hydrogen in the monomer unit by an electron-donating or electron-withdrawing group (methyl or Na sulphonyl) was studied. The type of glycosidic linkage between the monomer units of the polysaccharides having either (1→ 4)-β-D, (1→3)-β-D or (1→6)-α–D configuration and the linear or branched structure of polysaccharide on thermooxidative stability of polysaccharides have been compared. It has been shown that the least stable from the polymers examined were methylated cellulose and mannan, while the pure cellulose was the most stable. (1→6)-α–D linked polymers undergo predominantly to hydrolytic degradation rather than oxidation, provided that they have sufficiently high molar mass and have linear structure.

Key words: Thermal oxidation, polysaccharides, structural effects, chemiluminescence.

INTRODUCTION

Cellulose belongs to the most abundant natural organic materials. From the series of different polymers it is relatively stable with respect to thermooxidative degradation. However, the progress of the degradation process, which depends on temperature and concentration of oxygen, is complicated by a pronounced effect of various factors such as humidity, pH value, ionic admixtures, etc, and the ionic mechanism of degradation is always superposed with free radical degradation, the former being much faster than the latter. It is known that ionic process renders aldehydes which promote the free radical process leading to carboxylic acids which may play a significant role in an ionic process. For quantification of these effects, general approaches such as determination of the degree of polymerization, determination of functional groups such as carbonyls, carboxyls, etc., which are rather laborious are normally used. Within the 5th framework programme of EU, the chemiluminescence method (CL) was proposed as a method having the potential to throw some light on the complex mechanism of the degradation process of polysaccharidic materials. This method is based on the measurement of the light emitted from the degrading material and predominantly monitors the oxidation reactions of free radical character.

In spite of the numerous studies on chemiluminescence accompanying thermooxidation of many synthetic polymers [1-10], the light emission from cellulose or other polysaccharides was investigated to a lesser extent [11-14]. The pertaining problem is the mechanism of the chemical reactions ultimately leading to the light emission. It can be shown that the intensity of the light emission may be related to the rate of peroxyl radicals recombination which in the case of free radical oxidation is proportional to the rate of initiation. However, the initiation of oxidation may occur on atoms of backbone, as well as on the side-chain and terminal groups of the macromolecular chain, and thus the relation with the rate of the degradation leading to the scission of macromolecules do not need to be necessarily straightforward.

In our recent paper we have shown that the average rate constants determined from the kinetics of non-isothermal chemiluminescence runs for oxidation of cellulose in oxygen are well comparable with the rate constants determined from the decrease of the degree of polymerization [15]. Non-isothermal chemiluminescence runs were approximated by the sum of two parallel reactions being initiated from two kinds of reaction sites on the cellulose backbone, the faster and slower ones and the average rate constant was determined accordingly.

In the present paper we compare the chemiluminescence runs for 8 typical polysaccharides including pure cellulose and its more complex structures formed upon substitution of hydroxylic hydrogens with methyl and Na sulphonic groups and/or chitin-glucan complexes, together with glucan, mannan, pullulan and dextrane having (1→3)-β-D and (1→6)-α-D linkages binding glucopyranosyl and manopyranosyl units.

EXPERIMENTAL

Materials

Cellulose under study, Whatman, Maidstone, UK, was used as received. Cellulose is a linear poly (1→4)-β–D glucopyranose. The part of its chain may be seen on the above sketch.

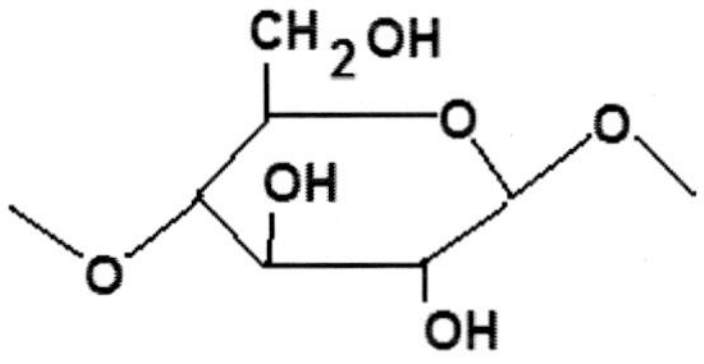

Figure 1. Structural unit of cellulose.

Methyl cellulose was purchased from Jena Bioscience, Germany. The degree of substitution with methyl groups was 2.8-2.9. Sulphonated cellulose (sodium salt) was purchased from Acros Organics, batch # A016485701, degree of substitution ~ 1.6, molar mass determined by viscosimetry was $8x10^5$ g/mol.

Pullulan samples of different molar masses (set of SEC standards) with molecular peaks at 5.8, 24, 48, 100, 212, 380 and 1600 kDa (kg/mol) were purchased from Fluka, Switzerland and used as received.

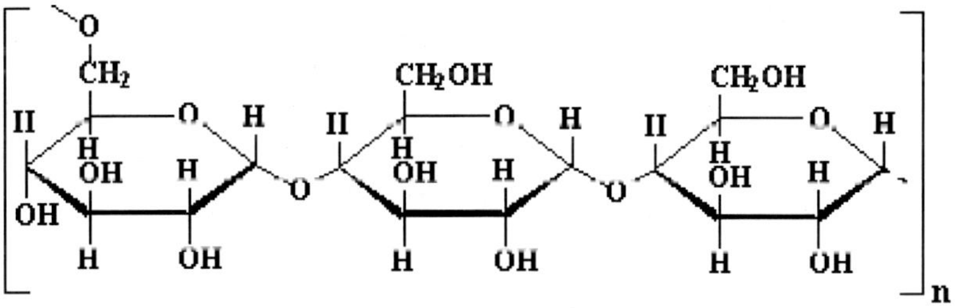

Figure 2. Structural unit of pullulan.

Pullulan is a (1→4,1→6)-α -D glucan containing (1→6)-α linked maltotriose structural units. Dextranes (from Polymer Standards Service GmBH) are branched poly-α-D-glucosides of microbial origin having predominantly (1→6) glycosidic bonds. Other polysaccharides are yeast glucan predominantlycomposed of (1→3)-β-D linked glucopyranosyl units, chitin-glucan complex from filamentous fungi, and yeast mannan having mainly (1→6)-α-D linked mannopyranosyl units

These substances were prepared according to the following procedures:

Isolation of the Chitin–glucan Complex

The crude, water-insoluble chitin–glucan complex was isolated from the cell walls of the industrial strain Aspergillus niger (Kaznejov, Czech Republic) by hot alkaline (1 M NaOH) extraction. Elemental analysis was performed using an EA 1108 instrument (Fisons Instruments, UK). The dry sample of chitin-glucan complex contained 2.24% of nitrogen, which corresponded to a content of ca. 30% chitin [16]. The structure of chitin is very similar to that of cellulose. Both involve (1→4)-β–D linked monosaccharide units. The difference between the cellulose monomer and that of chitin molecule is that chitin has 2-acetylamido group instead of 2-hydroxyl group in the glucosyl unit of cellulose.

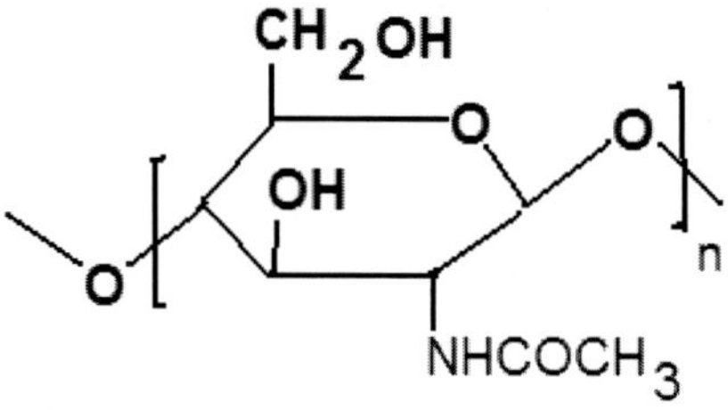

Figure 3. Structural unit of chitin

Isolation of β-D-glucan

The water-insoluble β-D-glucan was obtained by means of extraction of baker's yeast biomass (Saccharomyces cerevisiae) purchased from fy Slovlik (Trenčín, Slovak Republic). Saccharomyces cerevisiae cells were treated with 6% NaOH at 60 °C followed by 4% phosphoric acid extraction at room temperature as described by Kogan et al. [17]

Isolation of the Cell-wall Mannan

Candida albicans serotype B cells (Culture Collection of Yeasts, Institute of Chemistry, Slovak Academy of Sciences, Bratislava) were disintegrated by autoclaving at 140 °C with 0.2 M NaCl. The cell walls were separated by centrifugation and extracted with 2% KOH for 2 h at 100 °C. Cellular mannan was precipitated from the supernatant liquor with Fehling reagent. The mannan was purified as described by Kogan et al. [18]. All materials investigated were in powdered form.

DSC records in nitrogen of the prepared materials are presented in Figure 4. The first endotherms of all samples are obviously related to the release of residual water, while the second endotherm corresponds to sample melting. Mannan had the lowest temperature of the melting, while β–D-glucan the highest one.

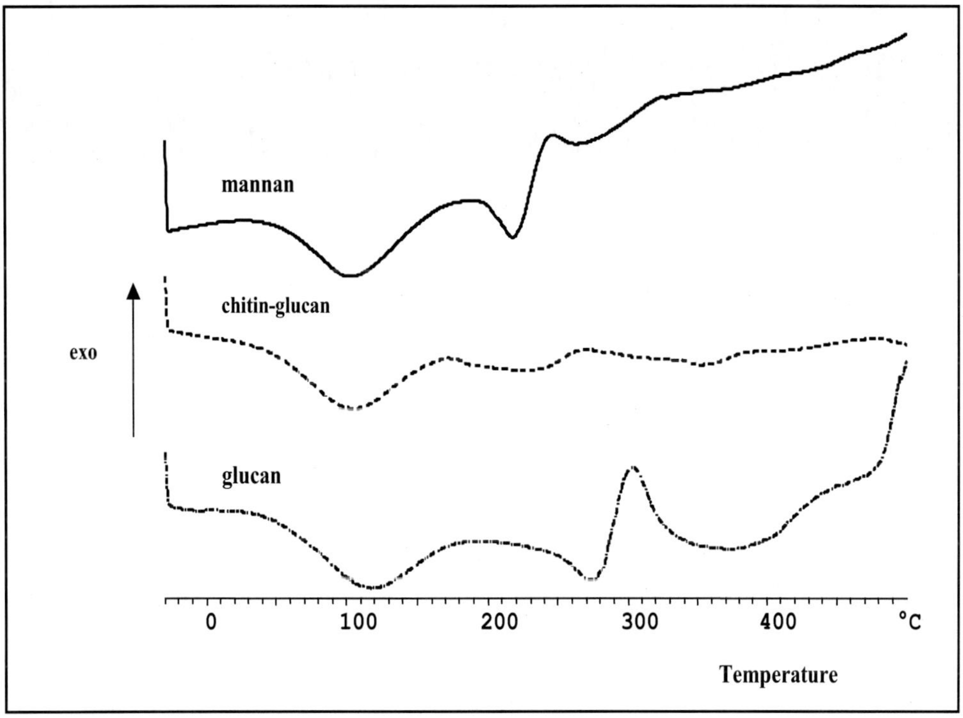

Figure 4. DSC records of chitin-glucan complex, β-glucan and mannan in nitrogen atmosphere

Measurements

CL measurements were carried out with the luminometer Lumipol 2, produced at Polymer Institute of SAS, Bratislava. The intensity of emitted light (in counts/s) was recorded under non-isothermal conditions as the records of intensity on temperature (the rate of heating was usually 2.5 °C/min) or in isothermal mode in oxygen or nitrogen atmosphere. The instrument dark count rate was 2-3 counts/s.

Samples of the initial weight (around 2 mg) were placed on aluminum pans of the diameter 9 mm and put into the oven of the CL apparatus; the gas flow through the sample was 3 l/h.

DSC measurements were carried out using a Mettler-Toledo DSC 821^e Differential Scanning Calorimeter in nitrogen and oxygen atmosphere (50 ml/min). The experiments were performed from – 30 to 500°C at a heating rate of 10°C/min.

Thermogravimetry was carried out using Mettler-Toledo TGA/SDTA 851^e thermobalance in nitrogen and oxygen atmosphere (30 ml/min) in the temperature range 25 – 500°C and at the heating rate 5°C/min.

EVALUATION OF KINETIC PARAMETERS FROM NON-ISOTHERMAL CHEMILUMINESCENCE RUNS

The kinetic approach to the chemiluminescence process is based on the simple initiation of oxidation reaction as follows:

$PH + O_2 \rightarrow$ products

in which there are formed HO_2 radicals and alkyl radicals P are formed from the main chain of the macromolecule. Provided that the chemiluminescence emission arises mainly from termination reaction of two peroxyl radicals which under stationary conditions is proportional to the rate of initiation, we have:

$$I = \mu\{-\frac{d[PH]}{dt}\} \tag{1}$$

where [PH] is the concentration of active sites on biopolymer molecule molecules and μ is a proportionality constant that takes into consideration the quantum yield of chemiluminescence process and the geometry of the sample. Active sites decay in the course of degradation and the degree of polymerization may be changed accordingly. The rate of the decay of active sites is proportional to the product of their concentration and concentration of O_2, i.e.:

$$-\frac{d[PH]}{dt} = k[PH][O_2]^n \tag{2}$$

where n is the order with respect to oxygen.

Provided that the concentration of oxygen which is in contact with the polymer surface remains constant, equation (2) can be modified to:

$$-\frac{d[PH]}{dt} = k_1[PH] \tag{3}$$

which is the first order process with respect to active sites on polymer molecules.

Equation (3) may be easily converted to non-isothermal conditions with the linearly increasing temperature as follows:

$$-\frac{d[PH]}{dT}\frac{dT}{dt} = k_1[PH] = A_1\exp(-\frac{E_1}{RT})[PH] \tag{4}$$

Here $\frac{dT}{dt} = \beta$ is the constant rate of heating and the rate constant k_1 is replaced by Arrhenius term with A_1 and E_1 as pre-exponential factor and activation energy, respectively. The pre-exponential factor is directly proportional to the square root of concentration of oxygen. The integration of equation (4) gives:

$$[PH] = [PH]_0 \exp[-\frac{A_1}{\beta}\int_{T_0}^{T}\exp(-\frac{E_1}{RT})dT] \tag{5}$$

If there are two or more kinds of active sites, such as those which undergo faster and slower degradation, as it may occur in simultaneously proceeding ionic and free radical degradation processes, then [PH] is the sum of concentrations of all types of active sites. For the case of three kinds of active sites we have:

$$[PH] = \sum_{j=1}^{3}[PH]_j = \sum_{j=1}^{3}[PH]_{0j} \exp[-\frac{A_{1j}}{\beta}\int_{T_0}^{T}\exp(-\frac{E_{1j}}{RT})dT] \tag{6}$$

The same is valid for the rates.

$$\frac{d[PH]}{dt} = \sum_{j=1}^{3}\frac{d[PH]_j}{dt} \tag{7}$$

By combination of eqs. (1), (3) and (6) we finally obtain:

$$I = \mu k_1[PH] = \mu\sum_{j=1}^{3}k_{1j}[PH]_j = \mu\sum_{j=1}^{3}[PH]_{0i}A_{1j}\exp(-\frac{E_{1j}}{RT})\exp[-\frac{A_{1j}}{\beta}\int_{T_0}^{T}\exp(-\frac{E_{1j}}{RT})dT] \tag{8}$$

If we replace the product of proportionality constants, which is proportional to the surface below the curve, with P_i, we get:

$$I == \sum_{j=1}^{3}P_i \exp(-\frac{E_{1j}}{RT})\exp[-\frac{A_{1j}}{\beta}\int_{T_0}^{T}\exp(-\frac{E_{1j}}{RT})dT] \tag{9}$$

Notice that in approximation of chemiluminescence intensity – temperature run the proportionality constant μ is assumed to be independent on temperature.

The averaged rate constant k_{av} is defined as:

$$k_{av} = \frac{P_1}{P_1+P_2+P_3}k_{11} + \frac{P_2}{P_1+P_2+P_3}k_{12} + \frac{P_3}{P_1+P_2+P_3}k_{13} \tag{10}$$

Here $k_{1i} = A_{1i}\exp(-\frac{E_{1i}}{RT})$

The above kinetic analysis has some advantages and at the same time disadvantages. By the use of the non-linear regression analysis program we may achieve a perfect fit with experimental chemiluminescence run and get for it the series of three rate constants characterized by corresponding activation energy and pre-exponential factor. Without going into further details which will be the subject of a separate study we may reveal by such an approach if the oxidation process is a typical autooxidation with accummulation of hydroperoxides or not. If this is the case, the activation energy obtained from the part of the curve under the largest surface of experimental chemiluminescence run attains abnormally high values due to the contribution of the autoacceleration to the light emission increase. On the other hand, fitting the resulting curve by several first order processes may lead to a certain compensation in parameters which becomes particularly evident when the measured curves are not well developped or somehow distorted.

RESULTS AND DISCUSSION

Figure 5 shows the shift of DSC degradation exotherms to lower temperatures in the case when hydroxyl hydrogens of glucopyranosyl units were substituted with Na salt of sulphonic acid (line 2) or with methyl groups (line 3). This shift is in a good agreement with that of chemiluminescence intensity runs performed by the heating of the sample in oxygen from 40 to 220 °C by the rate 2.5 °C/min (Figure 5). Maximum of the chemiluminescence run for methylated cellulose is at 192 °C while for DSC run it is at 190 °C. Na-sulphonated cellulose has a maximum at 209 °C for chemiluminescence experiment and at 220 °C for DSC run. The chemiluminescence accompanying the oxidation of methylated cellulose is considerably more intense (more than by one order of magnitude) than that for both Na-sulphonated or pure cellulose (Figure 6).

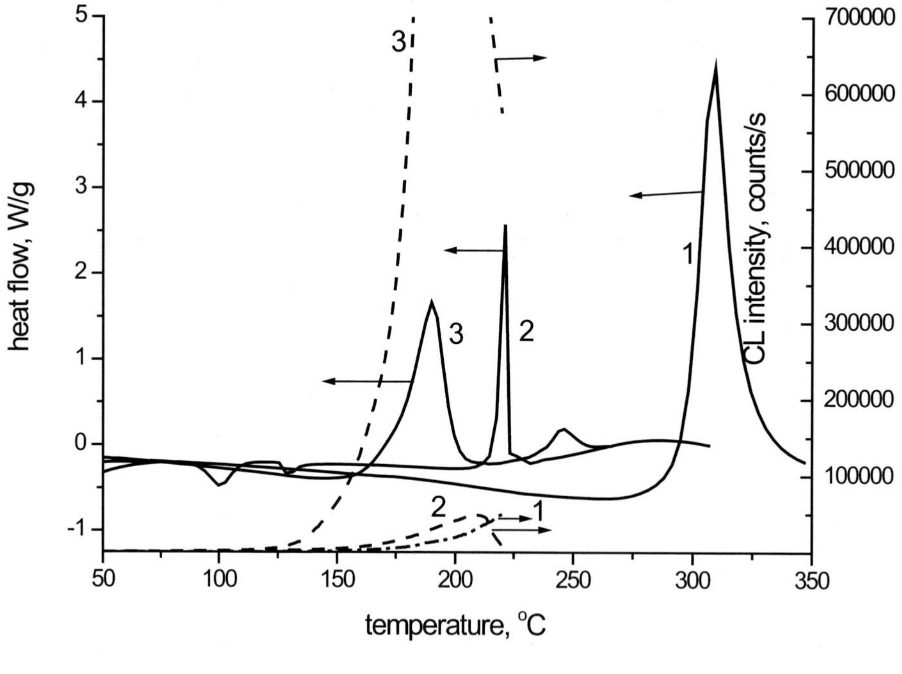

Figure 5. Comparison of chemiluminescence (heating rate 2.5 °C/min) and DSC (heating rate 10 °C/min) non-isothermal runs for cellulose (line 1), Na-sulphonyl cellulose (line 2) and methylated cellulose (line 3) in oxygen

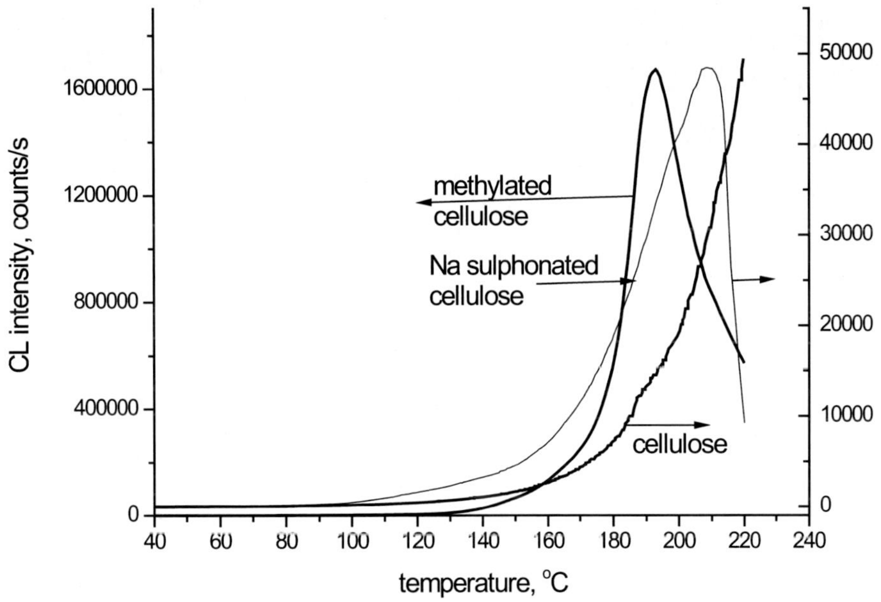

Figure 6. Comparison of non-isothermal chemiluminescence accompanying the oxidation of cellulose, methylated cellulose and Na-sulphonated cellulose in oxygen, the rate of heating 2.5 °C/min.

This probably indicates that the chemiluminescence phenomenon in its predominant extent is related to the oxidation of carbon atoms carrying hydrogens. In the case of methylated cellulose these hydrogens are those of methyl groups linked with the ether oxygen atom and of methylene group (C-6 of glucopyranose unit) while in the case of Na-sulphonated cellulose or cellulose it is only the oxidation of C-6 oxymethylene group in methylhydroxyl group of glucopyranose unit. This assumption is further confirmed by non-isothermal chemiluminiscence experiments on chitin-glucan complexes. In the molecule of chitin there are acetamido groups linked to glucopyranosyl unit containing methyl groups as well. As expected chemiluminescence intensity observed for chitin-glucan complexes is considerably stronger than that for glucan itself or mannan (Figure 7).

Kinetic parameters from chemiluminescence non-isothermal runs were determined for all samples of polysaccharides under the study. An example of the set of obtained parameters including the proportionality constants (surface below the curve area), pre-exponential factors and activation energy corresponding to each separate step for 6 basic polysaccharides is shown in Table 1.

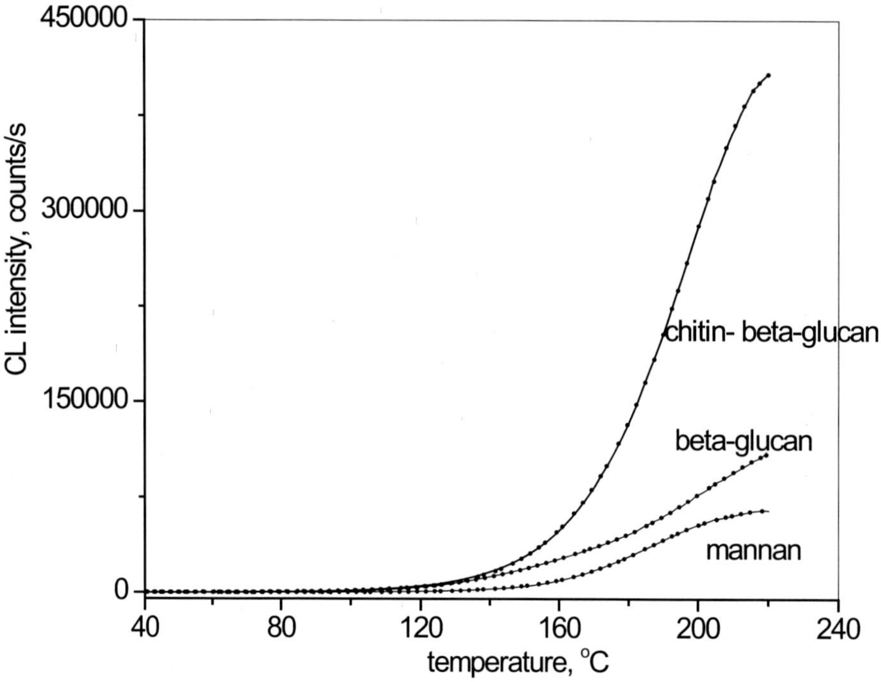

Figure 4. Non-isothermal CL runs for the polysaccharides in oxygen, the rate of heating, 2.5 °C/min, points represent theoretical fit by the sum of three first order processes according to equation (9)

Table 1. Parameters of Equation (9) Determined from Non-isothermal Chemiluminescence Runs for Oxidation of Individual Polysaccharides in Oxygen (the Rate of Sample heAting 2.5 °C/min)

Sample	P_1	P_2	P_3	A_{11}	A_{12}	A_{13}	E_{11}	E_{12}	E_{13}
	counts	counts	counts	s^{-1}	s^{-1}	s^{-1}	kJ/mol	kJ/mol	kJ/mol
Cellulose	2.52e7	7.75e7	5.47e5	161	1.21e10	3.76e39	52.4	125.0	369.7
Methylated cellulose	4.17e7	7.71e8	4.77e8	1.87e18	9.50e12	1.08e27	171.3	142.4	260.9
Na-sulphonated Cellulose	1.04e7	4.74e6	2.94e7	3250	5.08e53	1.9e13	55.3	517.0	143.8
Chitin-glucan	2.03e6	5.77e8	2.85e7	3.85e4	2.75e6	2.78e9	57.3	87.5	109.0
Glucan	6.81e6	1.77e8	1.96e7	1.81e7	5.67e5	6.29e5	81.3	82.2	74.9
Mannan	3.81e7	1.13e8	7.44e5	8.50e8	4.53e9	1.43e8	102.9	116.4	81.7

For each of the three independent first order processes, the rate constants were calculated for 150 and 180 °C and their average values were calculated using equation (10). The results are summarized in Table 2.

Table 2. Average Rate Constants k_{av} of the First Order Degradation Reaction of Some Biopolymers Obtained from Chemiluminescence experIments at 150 and 180 °C k_{av}, s^{-1}

Sample	150 °C	180 °C
Cellulose	1.87e-5	9.96e-5; 9.45e-5 from DP measurements
methylated cellulose	7.78e-5	0.0021
Na sulphonated cellulose	1.51e-4	7.77e-4
Chitin glucan complex	6.05e-5	3.25e-4
Glucan	1.43e-4	6.44e-4
Mannan	1.29e-4	7.93e-4
Pullulan, 5.6 kDa	5.2e-5	5.2e-4
Pullulan , 24 kDa	4.4e-5	3.3e-4; 3.49e-4 from molar mass measurements
Pullulan, 48 kDa	5.4e-5	3.9e-4; 5.78e-4 from molar mass measurements
Pullulan, 100 kDa	2.8e-5	1.3e-4; 8.83e-4 from molar mass measurements
Pullulan, 212 kDa	3.8e-5	2.3e-4
Pullulan, 380 kDa	2.1e-5	1.8e-4; 2.1e-3 from molar mass measurements
Pullulan, 1600 kDa	3.1e-5	1.6e-4; 2.18e-3 from molar mass measurements
Dextran, 9.9 kDa	7.1e-6	3.31e-5
Dextran, 21.4 kDa	7.7e-6	6.71e-5
Dextran, 43.5 kDa	1.66e-5	8.6e-5
Dextran, 123 kDa	4.22e-5	2.45e-4
Dextran, 1450 kDa	2.33e-5	1.07e-4

As can be seen, the average rate constants from chemiluminescence measurements for pullulan decrease with increasing initial molar mass (Figure 8), while opposite is true for dextran (except for that with the highest molar mass). Of the polymers examined, pure cellulose and dextran appears to be the most stable with respect to thermooxidation. A very low stability is revealed by methylated cellulose, Na-sulphonated cellulose, mannan and also pullulan of the lowest molar masses.

However, when one compares the average rate constants from non-isothermal chemiluminescence measurements and those obtained from decrease of the peak molar mass value or degree of polymerization it may be seen that while a good agreement is received for pure cellulose [15] the large discrepancy (by one order of magnitude) exists for high molar masses pullulans (Table 2, [19]). The example of the decay of number average molar mass for pullulan of the peak molar mass 1600 kDa and 48 kDa in oxygen at 180 °C is shown in Figure 9. From this Figure it is obvious that the decay of lower molar mass of pullulan is slower than that of pullulan of higher molar mass.

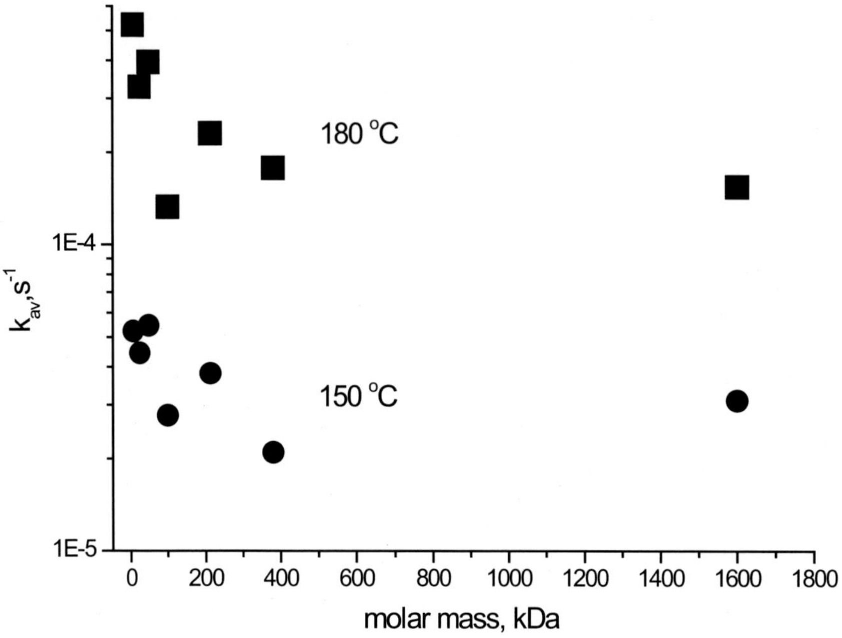

Figure 8. Plot of average first order rate constants obtained from chemiluminescence measurements of oxidation of pullulan in oxygen

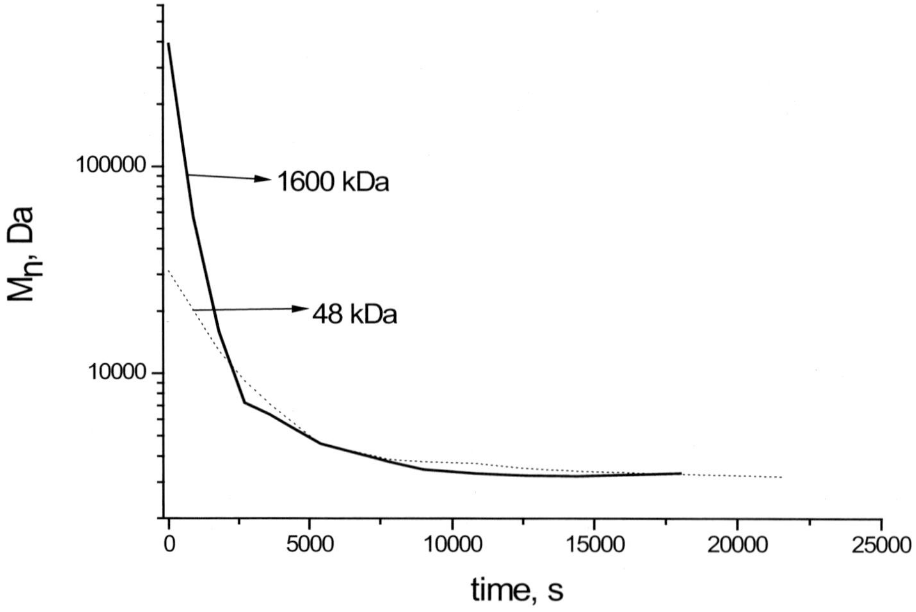

Figure 9. Decay of the number average molar mass for two pullulans differing in the peak molar mass in oxygen and at temperature 180 °C

From the observed agreement between the rate constants calculated from non-isothermal chemiluminescence measurements and those obtained from the decrease of the degree of polymerization it can be concluded that the chemiluminescence light emission comes from the termination of unequal peroxyl radicals of which one has a tertiary character according to the scheme in Figure 10. Under such conditions the main chain scissions of the macromolecules may take place and the mutual agreement between both kinds of experiments as it was observed for cellulose, is well comprehensible.

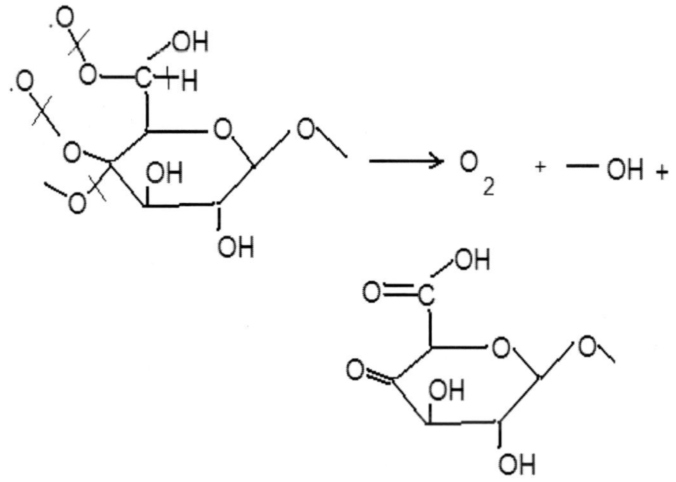

Figure 10.

On the other hand, discrepancy observed for high-molar-mass pullulans may be due to the fact that (1→6)-α linkage is hydrolytically rather unstable. This instability may be seen on the comparison of the GPC records of 1:1 mixtures of pullulans with molar masses 50 and 800 kDa in water which have been let for 6 weeks in a refrigerator (Figure 11). The higher molar mass fraction shifted to lower molar mass while the lower molar mass fraction remained practically unchanged. The threshold of this instability lies somewhere around 100 kDa since the rate constants determined from chemiluminescence and DP measurements were getting closer to each other in the case of molar mass 48 kDa while for pullulan with molar mass 100 kDa their values were still rather different (Table 2). In [19] it was described that the rate constants of degradation of pullulan measured by DP determination in nitrogen and oxygen were almost the same which strongly supports the idea of hydrolytical degradation of pullulan macromolecules by splitting their (1→6) glycosidic bonds. The hydrolytic stability of dextrans that also have (1→6)-α–D glycosidic linkages may be increased due to their extensively branched structures.

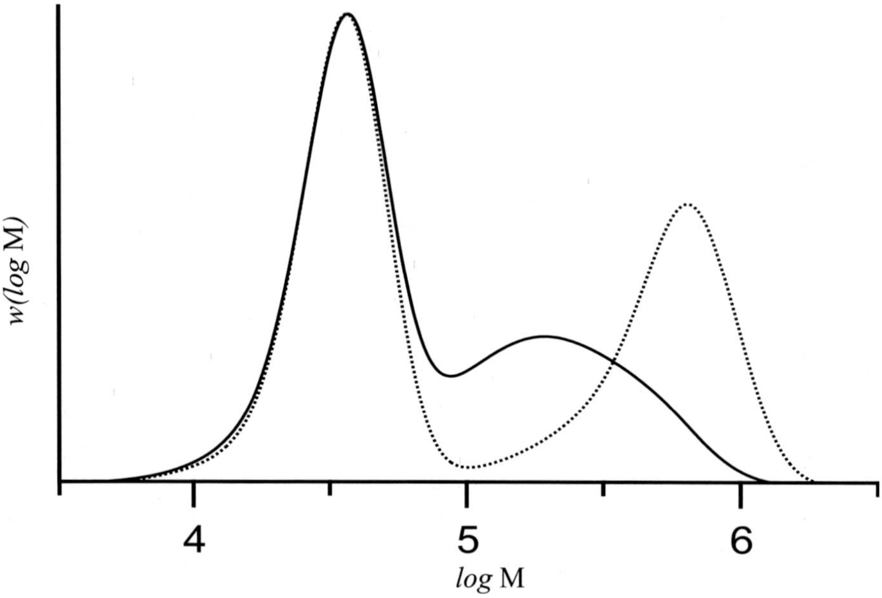

Figure 11. Comparison of GPC data of freshly prepared (dashed line) and 6 weeks stored in refrigerator (solid line) 1:1 mixture of pullulans of initial molar masses 50 and 800 kDa.

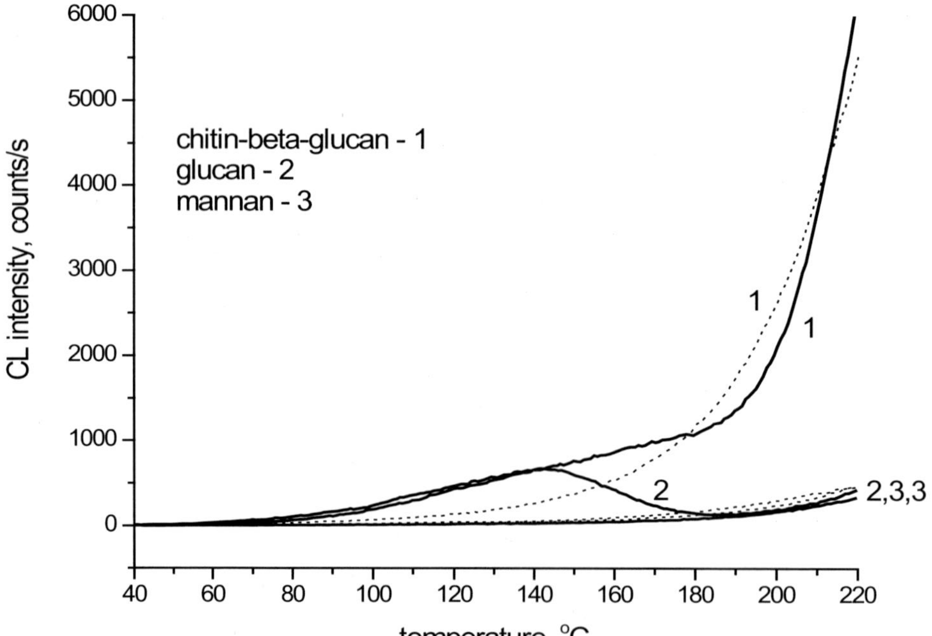

Figure 12. Chemiluminescence non-isothermal records of the first (full line) and the second (dotted line) cycle of heating of certain polysaccharides from 40 to 220 °C (5 °C/min)

In our paper [19] we have also expressed an idea that the intensity of peroxide peak observed by chemiluminescence in non-isothermal mode under nitrogen which appeared in the experiments with polysaccharides after their pre-oxidation in oxygen might correlate with the initial concentration of aldehydic groups in the original sample. Indeed, the observed peak was the largest for low-molar-mass pullulans while for the high-molar-mass compounds it was rather weak. The same appears to be true for chitin-glucan, glucan and mannan samples. If each sample was examined several weaks after its preparation it could be seen that chitin-glucan complex gave quite distinct chemiluminescence peak in nitrogen while mannan did not reveal anything. After the first heating this peak did not appear in the case of both chitin-glucan and glucan since all peroxides were already decomposed. As found from thermogravimetry measurements the decomposition of mannan into volatiles is practically independent on atmosphere of degradation (Figure 13). The same observation has been done with samples of pullulan. We have thus another possibility how to differentiate predominant hydrolytic degradation (no dependence on the concentration of oxygen) from thermo-oxidation degradation (a distinct shift of non-isothermal thermogravimetry experiments to lower temperatures in the presence of oxygen).

The correspondence with the intensity of peroxide peak in chemiluminescence non-isothermal experiments is also worth noticing.

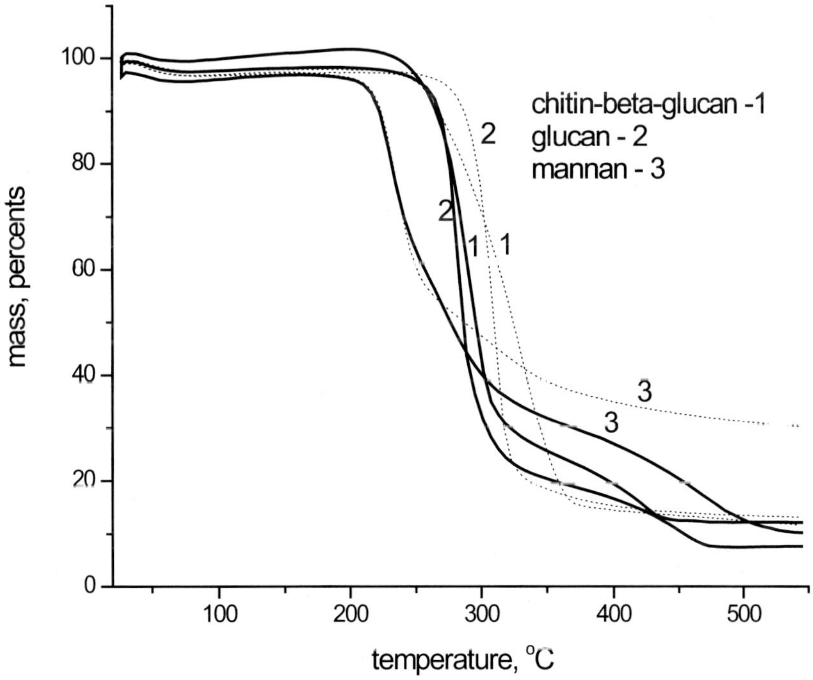

Figure 13. Non-isothermal thermogravimetry of certain polysaccharides in oxygen (full line) and in nitrogen (dotted line), heating rate 5 °C/min

Conclusions

The combined experiments of chemiluminescence, molar mass decrease and thermogravimetry may contribute to further understanding of the extent of both the hydrolytic and thermo-oxidation degradation during thermooxidation of various polysaccharides. While chemiluminescence reflects total oxidation process focused on all oxidizable groups or atoms in macromolecule, molar mass decrease indicates only main chain scissions and thermogravimetry due to its sensitivity with respect to oxidation atmosphere may decide which of the two processes is dominant. Averaged rate constants of the first order determined from the sum of three independent first order processes being responsible for the polysaccharide thermooxidative degradation may serve as a quantitative way of oxidative stability of different polysaccharides.

Acknowledgements

The authors gratefully acknowledge the support of the European Community, 5th Framework Energy, Environment and Sustainable Development programme, contract no. EVK4-CT-2000-00038 (PAPYLUM). The work is the sole responsibility of the authors and does not represent the opinion of the Community. The Community is not responsible for any use that might be made of the data appearing herein.

The paper was prepared with partial financial support from GrantAgency VEGA, Slovak Academy of Sciences, No. 2/3053/23.

References

[1] Billingham, N. C. and George, G. A., *J. Polym. Sci., Part B: Polym. Phys., 28*, 257-265, (1990).

[2] George, G. A., in: Grassie N., Editor; Developments in Polymer Degradation, Vol. 3., Barking, *Appl. Science Pub*., 173-206, (1981).

[3] Zlatkevich, L. (Editor): *Luminescence Techniques in solid state polymer research* (Chapters 3 and 4), Marcel Dekker, Inc, New York and Basel, 93-131 and 135-194, (1989).

[4] Matisová-Rychlá, L., Rychlý J., In: Clough, R. L., Billingham, N. C. and Gillen, K. T., editors. Advances in chemistry, *Series 249: Polymer durability, degradation, stabilization and life-time predictions.* Washington DC, ACS, 175-193, (1993).

[5] Hosoda, S., Kihara, H. and Seki, Y., in: Clough, R. L., Billingham, N. C. and Gillen, K. T., Editors. Advances in chemistry, Series 249: *Polymer durability, degradation, stabilization and life-time predictions*. Washington DC, ACS, 195-212, (1993).

[6] Audouin-Jirackova, L. and Verdu, J., *J. Polym. Sci., Part A, Polym. Chem., 25*, 1205-1217, (1987).

[7] Lacey, D. J. and Dudler, V., *Polym. Deg. Stab., 51*, 101-108 (1996).

[8] Setnescu, R., Jipa, S. and Osawa, Z., *Polym. Deg. Stab., 60*, 377-383, (1998).

[9] Tiemblo, P., Gomez-Elvira, J. M., Teyssendre, G., Massines, F. and Laurent, Ch., *Polym. Deg. Stab., 65*, 113-121, (1999).

[10] Matisová-Rychlá, L., Rychlý, J. and George, G. A., *Polym. Deg. Stab., 75*, 385-396, (2002).

[11] Kelly, G. B., Williams, J. C., Mendenhall, G. D. and Ogle, C. A., in: Kelly, G. B., Eby, R. K., Editors. Advances in chemistry series, vol. 95. Washington: Am.Chem.Soc. 117, (1979).

[12] Konoma, F., Cai, X., Osawa, Z., *Polym. Deg. Stab.,65*, 105-111, (2000).

[13] Strlič, M., Kolar,J.,Pihlar, B., Rychlý, J. and Matisová-Rychlá, L., *Polym. Deg. Stab. 72*, 157-162 (2001).

[14] Rychlý, J., Matisová-Rychlá, L. and Strlič, M., *Polym. Int., 49*, 981-986, (2000).

[15] 15. Rychlý, J., Strlič, M., Matisová-Rychlá, L. and Kolar, J., *Polym. Deg. Stab., 78*, 357- 367, (2002).

[16] 16. Machová, E., Kvapilová, K., Kogan, G. and Šandula, J., *Ultrason. Sonochem. 5*, 169-172 (1999).

[17] 17. Kogan, G., Alföldi, J.and Masler, L., *Biopolymers 27,* 1055-1063 (1988).

[18] 18. Kogan, G., Pavliak, V.and Masler, L., *Carbohydrate Res. 172*, 243-253 (1988).

[19] 19. Strlič, M., Kočar, D., Kolar, J., Rychlý, J. and Pihlar, B. *Carbohydrate Polymers, 54*, 221-228, 2003.

In: New Developments in Polymer Analysis, Stabilization… ISBN 1-59454-511-1
Editors: G.E. Zaikov and A. Jiménez, pp. 133-152

Chapter 10

SYNTHESIS AND CHARACTERIZATION OF NATURAL RUBBER/CLAY NANOCOMPOSITES

M. A. López-Manchado,* B. Herrero and M. Arroyo
Institute of Polymer Science and Technology, C/ Juan de la Cierva, Madrid, Spain

ABSTRACT

Rubber compounds based on natural rubber (NR) reinforced with octadecylamine-modified saponite have been prepared via co-vulcanization process and characterized by several techniques. The silicate nanolayers are exfoliated and uniformly dispersed in the polymer chains. Monsanto measurements have shown that the organoclay accelerates the vulcanization reaction and, furthermore, gives rise to a marked increase of the torque, indicating that the elastomer becomes more crosslinked in the presence of the organoclay. These results were corroborated by swelling measurements since a noticeable increase in the curing degree was observed when the organoclay was added to the rubber recipe. Moreover, thermodynamic parameters have shown an increase in the structural order of the nanocomposite. In addition, thermal analysis supports the assumption that the degree of curing of the elastomer increases in the presence of the organoclay. An appreciable increase of the involved heat during the curing reaction has been observed. Moreover, the Tg of the NR increases in the presence of the organoclay due to the confinement of the elastomer segment into the organoclay nanolayers, which restricts the mobility of the chains. Mechanical characterization shows the strong reinforcing effect of the organoclay with increments up to 350 % in the strength in relation to NR. The mechanical properties of NR with 10 phr organoclay are comparable to the compound with 40 phr carbon black. Moreover, the organoclay improves the strength of the NR without hardly any reduction in the elasticity of the material.

Key words: Polymer nanocomposite, natural rubber, organoclay, saponite

---

* Corresponding author. lmanchado@ictp.csic.es Tel: +34 91 5622900 Fax: +34 91 5644853

INTRODUCTION

Polymer nanocomposites (PNCs) are a class of materials with properties that offer a significant commercial potential due to their specific properties. Polymer nanocomposites are commonly defined as the combination of a polymer matrix resin and inclusions that have at least one dimension (length, width or thickness) in the nanometer size range. Three major characteristics define the basis of PNC performance: nanoscopically confined matrix polymer, nanoscale inorganic constituents, and nanoscale arrangement of these constituents. In recent years polymer/layered silicate nanocomposites have attracted great interest, both in industry and academia, because they often exhibit remarkable improvement in material properties when compared with virgin polymer or conventional micro and macro-composites [1-6]. These include combination of increased modulus, strength and heat distortion temperature without sacrificing impact resistance [7]. The heat distortion temperature of the nanocomposites increases by up to 100 ºC, extending the use of composite to higher temperature environments, such as for under-the-hood parts in automobiles. Additionally, improved barrier properties [8, 9] and swelling in solvents [10] have been reported for several nanocomposite systems. Finally, nanocomposites exhibit decreased thermal expansivity, permeability and flammability [11-14]. In contrast to traditional fillers such as talc, carbon black or mica, which normally require loadings of 20 wt % or more, these enhancements are achieved with less than 5 wt % addition of layered silicates.

Besides their improved properties, nanocomposite materials are also easily extruded or moulded to near-final shape, simplifying their manufacturing. Since high degrees of stiffness and strength are realized with far less high density inorganic material, they are much lighter compared to conventional polymer composites. This weight advantage could have significant impact on environmental concerns among many other potential benefits. For example, it has been reported that widespread use of PNCs by US vehicle manufactures could save 1.5 billion litters of gasoline over the life of one year's production of vehicles and reduce related carbon dioxide emissions by more than 10 billion pounds [15]. In addition, their outstanding combination of barrier and mechanical properties may eliminate the need for a multipolymer layer design in packaging materials, enabling greater recycling of food and beverage packaging.

STRUCTURE AND PROPERTIES OF LAYERED SILICATES

The commonly used layered silicates for the preparation of polymer nanocomposites belong to the family of 2:1 layered or phyllosilicates. Layered materials are potentially well suited for the design of hybrid composites, because their lamellar elements have high in-plane strength and stiffness and a high aspect ratio [16]. In addition, the silicate particles exhibit the ability to disperse into individual layers. Virtually all families of lamellar solids share these attributes, but smectite clays (e.g. montmorillonite, saponite, hectorite) have been the layered silicates chosen for polymer nanocomposites design for two principal reasons. Firstly, they exhibit a very rich intercalation chemistry, which allows them to be chemically modified and made compatible with organic polymers for dispersal on a nanometer length scale. Secondly, they occur ubiquitously in nature and can be obtained in mineralogically pure format at low cost. Smectite clays can also be synthesized under hydrothermal condition, but purified natural clays normally offer a cost advantage over synthetic analogues.

The crystal structure of a typical smectite clay nanolayer consists of two-dimensional layers where a central octahedral sheet of alumina or magnesia is fused to two external silica tetrahedron by the tip so that the oxygen ions of the octahedral sheet do also belong to the tetrahedral sheets. The layer thickness is around 1 nm and the lateral dimensions of these layers may vary from 300 Å to several microns or larger, depending on the particular layered silicate. These layers organize themselves to form stacks with a regular van der Waals gap in between them called the interlayer or the gallery, occupied by hydrated inorganic exchange cations (typically sodium or calcium). Due to the hydrophilicity of the clay, water molecules are usually also present between the layers. Details regarding the structure and chemistry of these layered silicates are provided in Figure 1 and Table 1, respectively.

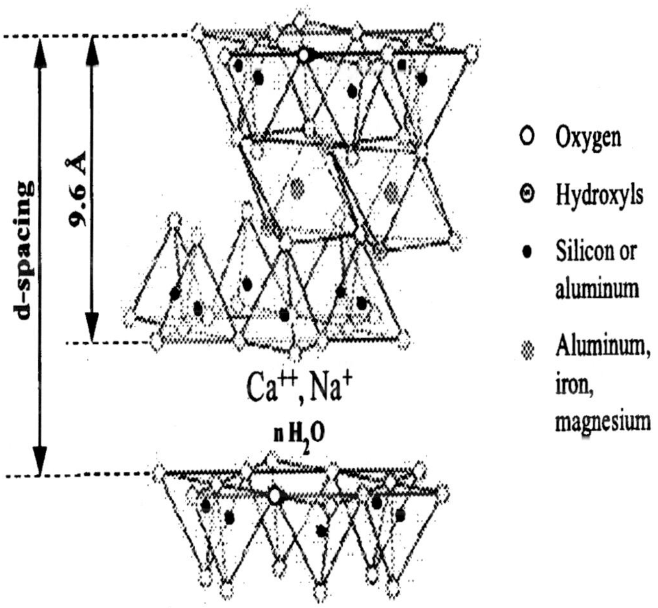

Figure 1. Structure of 2:1 phyllosilicates.

Table 1. Chemical Formula and Characteristics Parameter of 2:1 Phyllosilicates

2:1 phyllosilicates	Chemical formula	CEC (meq/100 g)	Particle length, nm
Montmorillonite	$M_x(Al_{4-x}Mg_x)Si_8O_{20}(OH)_4$	110	100-150
Hectorite	$M_x(Mg_{6-x}Li_x)Si_8O_{20}(OH)_4$	120	200-300
Saponita	$M_xMg_6(Si_8\text{-}xAl_x)Si_8O_{20}(OH)_4$	6.6	50-60

The same basic oxide lattice is also found in talc and mica. However, smectite clays are distinguished from talc and mica by a moderate negative layer surface charge (known as the cation exchange capacity, CEC, and generally expressed as meq/100 g), typically in the range from –0.6 to –1.4 per O_{20} unit) that is intermediate between the layer charge of talc (0.0 per

O_{20} unit) and mica (-2.0 per O_{20} unit). This intermediate value of layer charge leads to cation exchange and gallery swelling properties that are not shared by talc and mica. The charge of the layer is not locally constant, but varies from layer to layer, and must be considered as an average value over the whole crystal. It is obvious that the ion exchange property of smectites clays is an important aspect of their use in polymer nanocomposite preparation.

Organophilization of the Silicate

In order to develop polymer/clay nanocomposites with improved properties, at least two requirements must be satisfied. One is to separate the stacked layer structure of clay into monolayer if possible, in a polymer matrix. Thus, the aspect ratio of the filler particle increases and as a consequence of it, the reinforcement effects are enhanced [3]. Another is to control the interfacial affinity between a clay particle surface and the matrix polymer [4].

Obviously, in its pristine state, layered silicates are only miscible with hydrophilic polymers, such as poly(ethylene oxide) [17] or poly(vinyl alcohol) (PVA) [18]. To render layered silicates miscible with other polymer matrices, the normally hydrophilic silicate surface must be converted to an organophilic one by ion-exchange reactions of the hydrated cations of the interlayer by cationic surfactants. As the forces that hold the stacks together are relatively weak, the intercalation of small molecules between the layers is relatively easy. The clay so formed is commonly known as organoclay. The first compatibilizing agents used in the synthesis of nanocomposites (polyamide 6/clay hybrids) were amino acids [19]. Numerous other kinds of compatibilizing agents have since been used in the synthesis of nanocomposites. The most popular are long chain alkylammonium or alkylphosphonium salts because they can be easily exchanged with the cations located between the layers. The addition of alkylammonium cations in the organosilicates lower the surface energy of the inorganic host and improve the wetting characteristics of the polymer matrix, and result in a larger interlayer spacing. Additionally, these cations can provide functional groups that can react with the polymer matrix, or in some cases initiate the polymerisation of monomers to improve the strength at the inorganic/polymer matrix interface [20, 21].

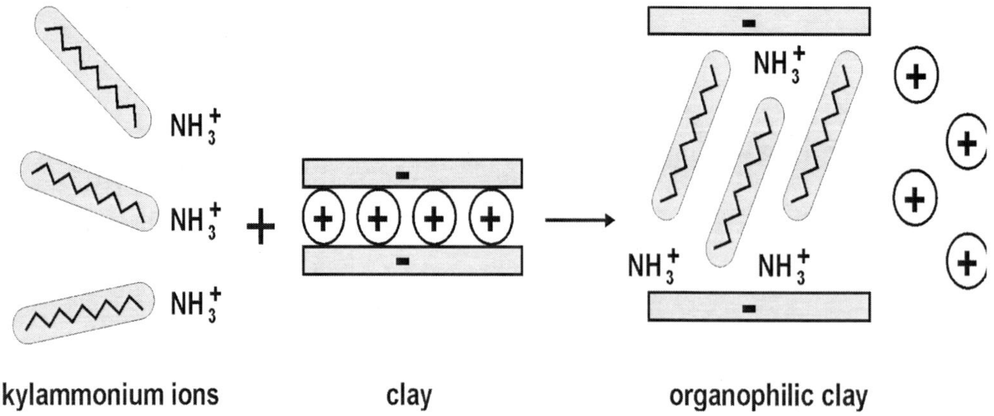

Figure 2. The cation-exchange process between alkylammonium ions and metallic cations

The most widely used alkylammonium ions are based on primary alkylamines put in acid medium to protonate the amine function. Their basic formula is CH_3-$(CH_2)_n$-NH_3^+ where n varies from 1 and 18. It is interesting to note that the length of the ammonium ions has a strong impact on the resulting structure of nanocomposites. Lan et al. [22] showed, for instance, that alkylammonium ions with chain length larger than eight carbon atoms were favouring the synthesis of delaminated nanocomposites whereas alkylammonium ions with shorter chains lead to the formation of intercalated nanocomposites. The cation-exchange process of linear alkylammonium ions is described in Figure 2.

Depending on the packing density, temperature and alkyl chain length, the alkylammonium ions adopt different structures between the clay layers (monolayers, bilayers, pseudotrimolecular layers, and paraffin type monolayers) (Figure 3) [23].

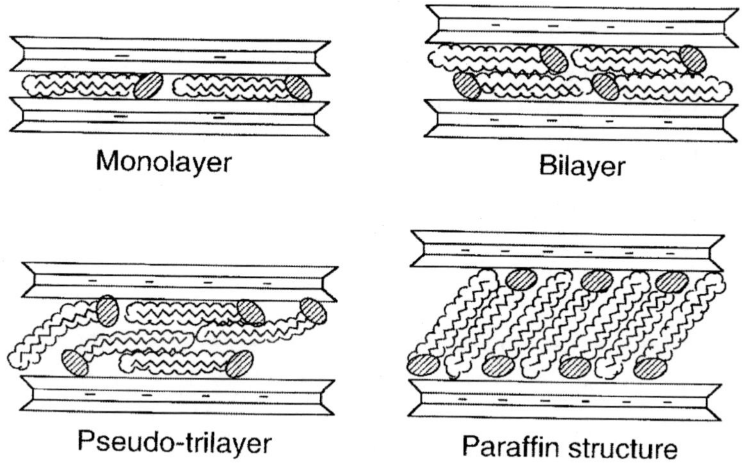

Figure 3. Arrangements of alkylammonium ions in layered silicates with different charge

SYNTHESIS OF POLYMER/CLAY NANOCOMPOSITES

It has been shown that the silicate layers of a clay mineral can be dispersed on a nanometer scale in an engineering polymer. The preparative methods for the synthesis of polymer/clay nanocomposites are included into four main groups according to the starting materials and processing techniques:

In-situ Polymerization

In-situ polymerization was the first method used to synthesize polymer/clay nanocomposites based on polyamide 6 [19]. Nowadays, it is a conventional process used to synthesise thermoset-clay nanocomposites. The mechanism is schematically described in Figure 4. In this method, the layered silicate is swollen within the liquid monomer or a monomer solution so the polymer formation occurs between the intercalated sheets. This step requires a certain amount of time, which depends on the polarity of the monomer molecules, the surface treatment of the organoclay, and the swelling temperature. Then, the reaction is initiated. For thermosets such as epoxies or unsaturated polyesters, a curing agent or a peroxide, respectively, is added to initiate the polymerization. For thermoplastics, the polymerization can be initiated either by the addition of a curing agent or by an increase of temperature [8]. Polymerization of a monomer occurs in the interlayer of the clay mineral, resulting in an expanded interlayer distance and silicate layers are homogeneously dispersed at a nanometer level at the end of the polymerization.

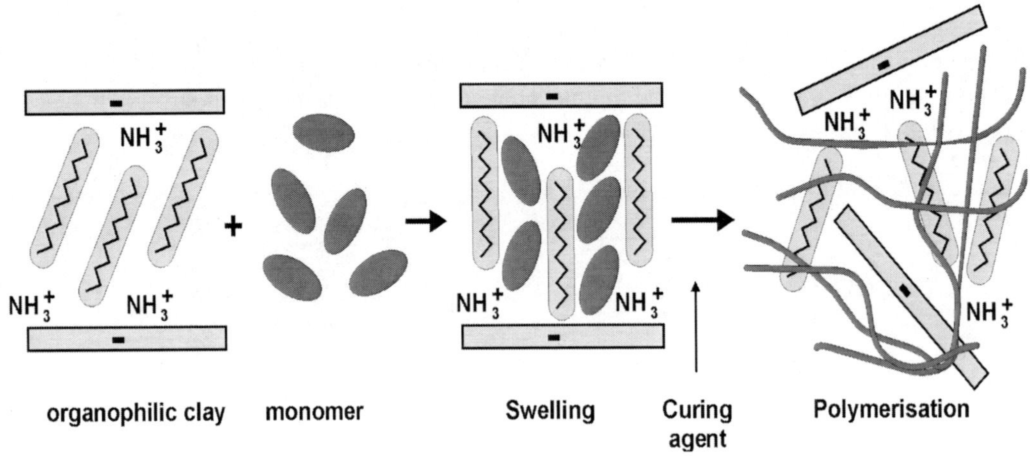

Figure 4. In-situ polymerization method

The key of the process is to control the polymerization between the layers (intragallery polymerization). If the cure kinetic between the layers is lower than outside the layers (extragallery polymerization), then delamination of the clay is impeded. Therefore, it is very important to find a method that favours the intragallery polymerization. The driving force of the "in-situ polymerization" method is linked to the polarity of the monomer molecules and is believed to be as follows: during the swelling phase, the high surface energy of the clay attracts polar monomer molecules so they are diffused between the clay layers. When a certain equilibrium is reached the diffusion stops and the clay is swollen in the monomer to a certain extent corresponding to a perpendicular orientation of the alkylammonium ions into the galleries [24]. When the polymerization is initiated, the monomer starts to react with the curing agent. This reaction lowers the overall polarity of the intercalated molecules and displaces the thermodynamic equilibrium so that more polar molecules are driven between the layers. As the process progress, the organic molecules can eventually delaminate the clay.

Solution

This method is based on a solvent system in which the polymer or pre-polymer is soluble and the silicate layers are swellable. The mechanism is similar to the "in-situ polymerization" approach. The layered silicate is first swollen in a solvent, such as water, chloroform, or toluene. Alkylammonium treated clays swell considerably in polar organic solvents, forming gel structures. When the polymer and the layered silicate solutions are mixed, the polymer chains intercalate and displace the solvent within the interlayer of the silicate. Upon solvent removal, the intercalated structure remains, resulting in a polymer nanocomposite. Figure 5 shows how the polymer is intercalated between the clay layers.

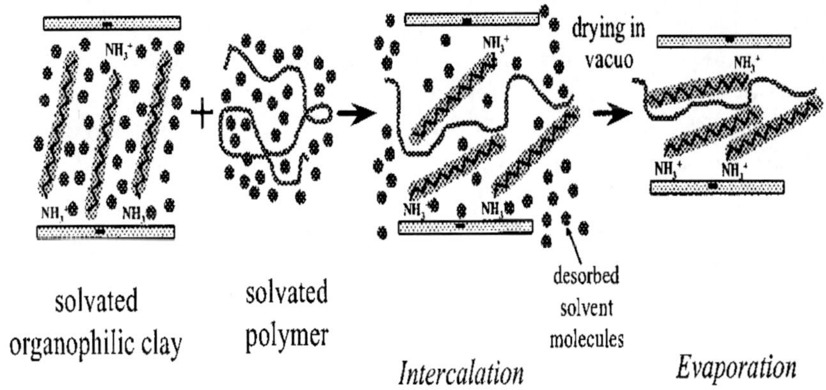

Figure 5. Solution method.

The driving force for intercalation from solution polymerization is the entropy gained by desorption of solvent molecules, which compensates the decrease in conformational entropy of the intercalated polymer chains [25]. Therefore, a relatively large number of solvent molecules need to de desorbed from the clay to accommodate the incoming polymer chains. The major advantage of this method is that it offers the possibilities to synthesise intercalated nanocomposites based on polymers with low or even no polarity, and facilities production of thin films with polymer-oriented clay intercalated layers. However, the solution method is difficult to apply in industry due to problems associated with the use of large quantities of solvent, which is usually environmentally unfriendly and economically prohibitive.

Co-vulcanization Method

Vulcanized rubbers are usually reinforced by carbon blacks to improve mechanical properties and also by inorganic minerals with some limitations. Carbon blacks are excellent in reinforcement owing to strong interaction with rubbers, but they often decrease the processability of rubber compounds at high volume loading. On the other hand, minerals have a variety of shapes suitable for reinforcement, such as needles and sheets, but they have only poor interaction with rubber. Therefore, it is interesting to disperse the silicate layers of the smectite on a nanometer level. In this method, the organophilic smectite was blended with the rubber by roll milling in the presence of all ingredients of the vulcanization (processing aids, antioxidants, accelerators, vulcanizing agents, etc). Then, the rubber was vulcanized by heating. A more detailed description of this method will be made later on this chapter.

Melt Intercalation Method

The melt intercalation process was first reported by Vaia et al [26] in 1993. The strategy consists in blending a molten thermoplastic with an organoclay in order to optimize the polymer/clay interactions. The mixture is then annealed above the softening point of the polymer, statically or under shear. While annealing, the polymer chains diffuse from the bulk polymer melt into the galleries between the silicate layers. The fact that polymer chains undergo centre of mass transport in between the clay layers is surprising because the unperturbed radius of gyration of the polymer is roughly an order of magnitude greater than the interlamellar spacing [27]. As shown in Figure 6, the polymer chains experience a dramatic loss of conformational entropy during the intercalation. The proposed driving force for this mechanism is the important enthalpic contribution of the polymer/organoclay interactions during the blending and annealing steps.

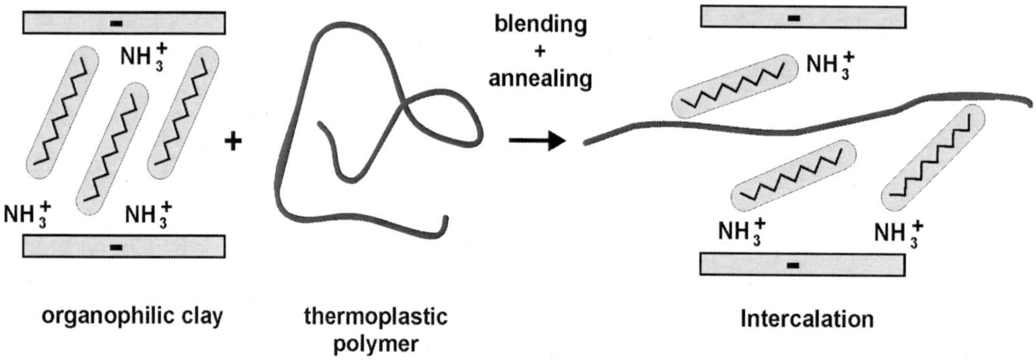

Figure 6. Melt intercalation approach

This method shows great advantages in comparison with in situ polymerization or polymer solution intercalation. First, this method is environmentally benign due to the absence of organic solvents and economically favourable for industries from a waste perspective. Second, it is compatible with current industrial process, such as extrusion and injection moulding. Besides, the melt intercalation method is highly specific for the polymer, leading to new hybrids which were previously nor suitable for in-situ polymerization or solution intercalation.

TYPES OF NANOCOMPOSITES

In general, layered silicates have layer thickness on the order of 1 nm and a very high aspect ratio (eg. 10-1000). A few weight percent of layered silicates that are properly dispersed throughout the polymer matrix thus create much higher surface area for polymer/filler interaction as compared to conventional composites.

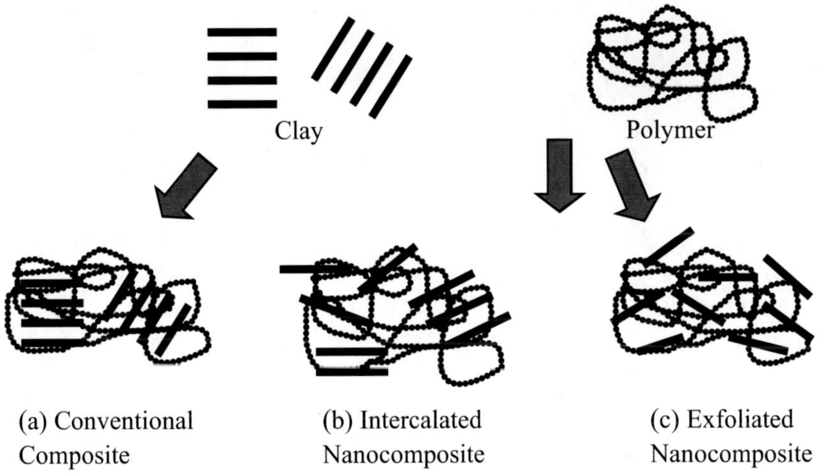

Figure 7. Different types of polymer/layered silicate nanocomposites

From a structural point of view, three main types of composites may be obtained when a layered clay is associated with a polymer:

(i) Conventional composite. The polymer is unable to intercalate between the silicate sheets and then, phase separated composite is formed (Figure 7a). Consequently, the clay fraction plays little or no functional role and acts mainly as a filling agent for economic considerations. An improvement in modulus is usually achieved, but this benefit is normally accompanied with a sacrifice in other properties, such as strength or elasticity.

(ii) Intercalated nanocomposites (Figure 7b) in which, one or a few polymer chains are intercalated into the clay galleries with fixed interlayer spacings. A well ordered multiplayer morphology is formed with alternating polymeric and inorganic layers.

(iii) Exfoliated nanocomposites (Figure 7c) are formed when the silicate nanolayers are individually dispersed in a continuous polymer matrix. The separation between the exfoliated nanolayers may be uniform (regular) or variable (disordered). Exfoliated nanocomposites show greater phase homogeneity than intercalated nanocomposites.

It is important to note that, in an exfoliated nanocomposite each nanolayer contributes fully to interfacial interactions with the matrix. This structural distinction is the primary reason why the exfoliated clay state is specially effective for the reinforcement of clay composite materials.

Characterization of Nanocomposites

The structure of polymer/clay nanocomposites is primarily characterized by using two techniques: X-ray diffraction analysis (WAXD) and transmission electron microscopy (TEM). Due to its easiness and availability WAXD is most commonly used to probe the nanocomposite structure and occasionally to study the kinetic of the polymer melt intercalation [28]. This is the best method to evaluate the spacing between the clay layers by application of the Bragg's Law, which is given:

$$n\lambda = 2d\sin\theta \quad (1)$$

where the integer n refers to the degree of the diffraction, λ is the wavelength, d is the interlamellar spacing or d-spacing and the experimental 2θ value is the angle between the diffracted and incoming X-ray waves. In addition, WAXD allows to determine the nanocomposite structure. For example, in an exfoliated nanocomposite, the extensive layer separation associated with the delamination of the original silicate layers in the polymer matrix results in the eventual disappearance of any coherent X-ray diffraction from the distributed silicate layers.

Although WAXD offers a convenient method to determine the interlayer spacing of the silicate layers in the original layered silicates and in the intercalated nanocomposites (within 1-4 nm), little can be said about the spatial distribution of the silicate layers or any structural non-homogeneities in nanocomposites. Additionally, some layered silicates do not exhibit well-defined basal reflections. Thus, peak broadening and intensity decreases are very difficult to study systematically. Therefore, it is necessary to be very careful when interpreting the results. Lack of sensitive of the analysis and limits of the equipment can lead to wrong conclusions about the nanocomposite structure. So, transmission electron microscopy is a necessary complement to X-ray diffraction. TEM allows a qualitative understanding of the internal structure, spatial distribution of the various phases, and views structure defects through direct visualisation but it requires substantial skills in specimen preparation and analysis. TEM is a powerful technique to analyze structures at and below the nanometer scale. Therefore it can be used to confirm results obtained by XRD about the organisation of the clay layers in the nanocomposite. It allows a precise observation of nanostructures with an exceptional resolution (about 0.2 nm). Therefore, this technique is widely used to characterize polymer/nanocomposites.

Another techniques used for the characterization of nanocomposites structures are:

- Scanning electron microscope (SEM)
- Thermogravimetric analysis (TGA)
- Solution and Solid-State NMR Spectroscopy
- Small angle scattering techniques: neutron and X-ray

PROPERTIES OF POLYMER/CLAY NANOCOMPOSITES

The increasing interest devoted to polymer/clay nanocomposites arises from the fact that the delamination of a relatively low amount of clay frequently exhibit remarkably improved mechanical and physical properties when compared to those of pristine polymers containing a small amount (≤ 5 wt%) of layered silicate. Improvements include a higher modulus, increased strength and heat resistance, decreased gas permeability and flammability, and increased biodegradability of biodegradable polymers. The main reason for these improved properties in nanocomposites is the stronger interfacial interaction between the matrix and layered silicate, in comparison with conventional filler-reinforced systems.

SYNTHESIS AND CHARACTERIZATION OF NATURAL RUBBER/CLAY NANOCOMPOSITES

The reinforcement of rubbers is expressed by enhancement of the modulus, failure properties (tensile and tear strength), and abrasion resistance of the vulcanizates. The main aim for filler addition is to improve certain properties and cheapen the compound. Among several fillers, carbon black is the most important reinforcing agent used in the rubber industry. Because of its origin from petroleum, carbon black causes pollution and gives the rubber a black colour. In the last two decades, research was focused on the development of other reinforcing agents to replace carbon black in rubber compounds. Sepiolite, kaolin and precipitated silica were commonly used as reinforcing agents. However, their reinforcing properties are lower than those of carbon black. Because of their inorganic nature, these mineral fillers are not compatible with polymer matrices. Since introducing of organophilic clays, polymer layered nanocomposites have focused the attention of researchers. Layered silicates dispersed at a nanosize level provide an effective reinforcement to rubber materials, improving the mechanical properties and barrier properties as compared to pristine rubber. However, there are hardly any reports on the preparation and dispersion of nanolayered silicates into natural rubber (NR) [29-31]. In this chapter, the synthesis and characterization of natural rubber/clay nanocomposites obtained via co-vulcanization process is described. It could be of great interest to use white fillers as substitutes for carbon black in rubber compounding.

PREPARATION PROCEDURE

The clay used is a saponite (Tolsa S.A., Spain under the trade mane BCA, clay) with a cation exchange capacity (CEC) value of 70 mequiv./100 g). In order to increase the interlayer spacing, the clay has been treated in our laboratories with octadecylamine (Aldrich) following a previously described procedure [29]. The ion-exchanged BCA (organoclay) was washed repeatedly with methanol until chlorine ions were not detected. Figure 8 shows the X-ray diffractions patterns of the clay (a) and organoclay (b). The clay shows a diffraction peak at $2\theta = 7^o$, which is assigned to the interlayer platelet spacing (001 diffraction peak), corresponding to an interlaminar distance of 12.6 Å, by applying Bragg's law. When the intercalating reagent is added, a displacement of the peak to lower angles ($2\theta = 5^o$) is observed. This corresponds to an interlayer spacing of 17.6 Å. It is assumed that the octadecylamine behaves as an effective intercalating agent, delaminating the saponite.

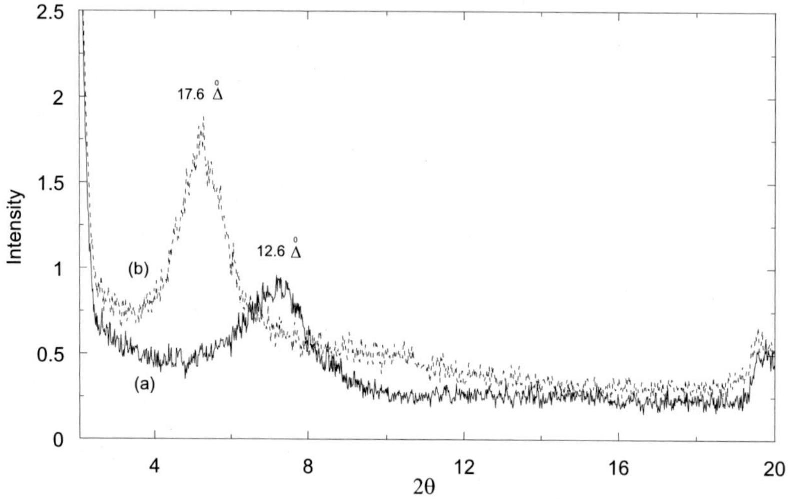

Figure 8. XRD patterns of clay (a) and organoclay (b)

The fillers were blended with natural rubber (supplied by Malasyam Rubber under the trade name CV 60, NR), in an open two-roll mill at room temperature. The rotors operated at a speed ratio of 1:1.4. The vulcanization ingredients were added to the elastomer previously to the incorporation of the filler and, finally, sulphur was added. The recipes of the compounds are shown in Table 2. The filler content was 10 phr (parts per hundred rubber). Rubber compounds were vulcanized at 160 ºC in a thermofluid heated press for the time previously determined on a Monsanto Moving Die Rheometer MDR 2000E.

Table 2. Recipes of the Rubber Compounds

Natural rubber	100	100	100	100	100
Zinc oxide	5	5	5	5	5
Stearic acid	1	1	1	1	1
Sulphur	2.5	2.5	2.5	2.5	2.5
MBTS[1]	1	1	1	1	1
PBN[2]	1	1	1	1	1
Unmodified clay	—	10	—	—	---
Organoclay	—	—	10	—	—
Carbon black	—	—	—	10	40

[1] Benzothiazyl disulfide.
[2] Phenyl beta naphtyl amine.

Nanocomposite Structure

Figure 9 shows X-ray diffraction profiles of the composites. The clay/composite showed a peak about 2θ= 7º, which corresponds to the interlayer spacing of the silicate. According to these results, the formation of a conventional composite at a microscopic scale, where the polymer is not intercalated into the silicate galleries, can be assumed. However, in the case of the NR/organoclay nanocomposite, this peak disappeared due to the higher layer spacing by insertion of the elastomer into the galleries of the organophilic saponite. In other words, the elastomer chains are confined within the layered silicate, forming a delaminated or exfoliated structure. As result, it can be concluded that the co-vulcanization method is very effective for the preparation of a clay/rubber nanocomposite.

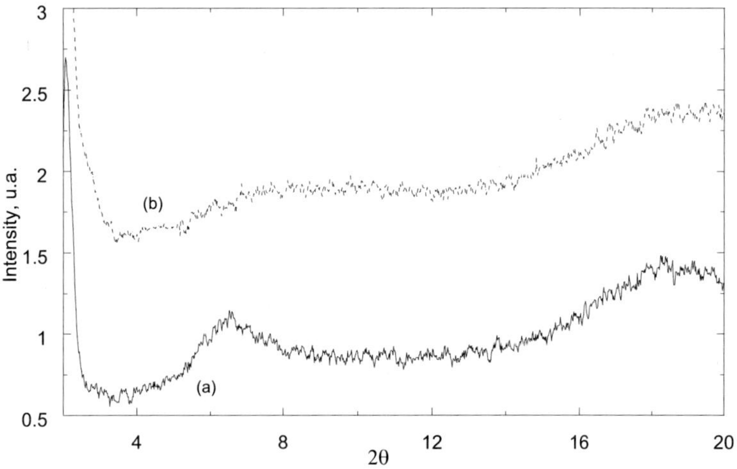

Figure 9. XRD patterns of NR/clay (a) and NR/organoclay (b) composites

NANOCOMPOSITE PROPERTIES

Vulcanization Characteristics of Compounds

The curing behaviour of the composites was analyzed at 160 °C on a Monsanto oscillating disc curemeter (Figure 10). It can be observed that unmodified clay hardly varies the cure characteristics of the rubber, probably due to a poor compatibility between the unmodified clay and hydrophobic polymer. However, the optimum cure time was sharply reduced in presence of the organoclay. That is, the organoclay behaves as an effective accelerant agent for NR vulcanization. This effect is attributed to the ammonium groups of the organic cations. In fact, amine groups facilitate the curing reaction of SBR and natural rubber stocks [32]. The cure time also gradually decreases when the carbon black content in the composites increased but to a smaller extent. The torque value increases in the presence of both fillers, being more noticeable with the organoclay. The nanocomposite with 10 phr of organoclay shows higher torque values than the counterpart with 40 phr of carbon black. Assuming that the torque value is intimately related to the crosslinking density, it can be concluded that the organoclay nanocomposites show a higher number of crosslinks than those with carbon black.

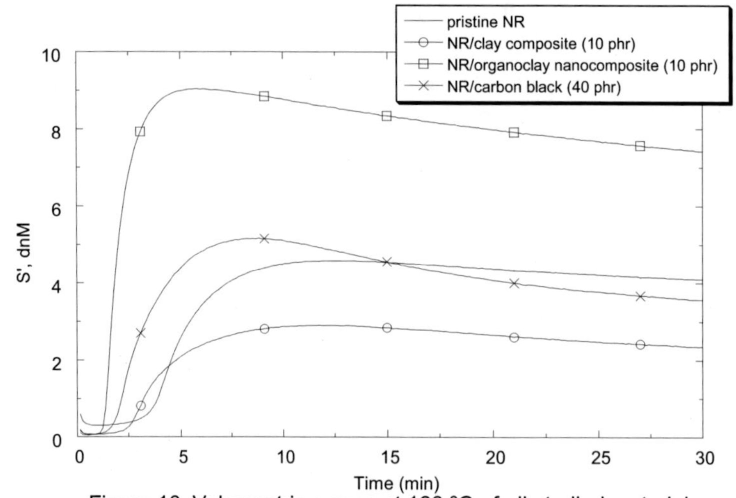

Figure 10. Vulcametric curves at 160 ºC of all studied materials

Crosslinking Density and Thermodynamical Parameters

The effect of the incorporation of the clay and organoclay on the crosslinking density of the natural rubber can be estimated by application of Flory-Rhener equation [33]:

$$-\left[Ln(1-\phi_r)+\phi_r+\chi\phi_r^2\right]=V_0 n\left[\phi_r^{1/3}-\frac{\phi_r}{2}\right] \quad (2)$$

where Φ_r is the volume fraction of polymer in the swollen mass, V_0 is the molar volume of the solvent (106.2 for toluene and 143.0 for n-heptane), and χ is the Flory-Huggins polymer-solvent dimensionless interaction term (0.393 and 0.460 for toluene and n-heptane, respectively. The volume fraction of polymer, Φ_r, is calculated by the following expression:

$$\Phi_r=\frac{W_i-W_w}{(W_i-W_w)+\left(\dfrac{W_S-W_i}{\rho_s}\right)} \quad (3)$$

where W_i, W_s and W_w are weights of the rubber samples in air, swollen state and immersed in water, respectively, and ρ_S is the solvent density (0.87 for toluene and 0.71 for n-heptane). In the case of the composites, the volume fraction of the filler, was previously calculated through the equation:

$$\Phi_f=(W_i-W_w)-\frac{W_i-a}{b\rho_f} \quad (4)$$

where *a* are the phr of the filler in the formulation, *b* is the total weight of the compound and ρ_f is the filler density, 2.05 gcm^{-3}. The obtained results of the volume fraction of the rubber, Φ_r, and crosslinking density, *n*, for the studied materials are reported in Table 3. According to these results, it can be deduced that in the presence of the clay a slight decrease in crosslinking density is observed as compared to pure NR. However, the crosslinking density sensibly increases when the organoclay is added to the polymer. These results are in agreement with those obtained from Monsanto measurements.

Table 3. Curing Degree and Thermodynamical Characteristics of the Studied Materials

	ϕ_r		N		ΔG, Jmol^{-1}		ΔS, Jmol^{-1}K^{-1}	
	toluene	**heptane**	**toluene**	**heptane**	**toluene**	**heptane**	**toluene**	**heptane**
NR	0.161946	0.22315	$8.97*10^{-5}$	$9.23*10^{-5}$	-11.13	-16.25	$3.67*10^{-2}$	$5.36*10^{-2}$
NR/clay	0.127181	0.18144	$3.98*10^{-5}$	$3.93*10^{-5}$	-6.27	-9.13	$2.06*10^{-2}$	$3.01*10^{-2}$
NR/organoclay	0.209615	0.27165	$1.61*10^{-4}$	$1.56*10^{-4}$	-21.04	-28.66	$6.94*10^{-2}$	$9.46*10^{-2}$

Thermodynamical aspects occurred during swelling of the elastomer chains were also analyzed. The thermodynamic is of great importance for the understanding of the rubber/filler interaction in the nanocomposite. It is well known that a crosslinked elastomer cannot be dissolved but it can be swelled in several solvents. This swelling depends on the elastomer crosslinking density and solvent used. So, a highly crosslinked material will show a limited swelling, but if the material presents a low crosslinking density, then, a higher swelling degree will be expected. This expansion of the rubber in the presence of a solvent will significantly modify the conformational entropy *(ΔS)*, and the elastic Gibbs free energy *(ΔG)*. The elastic Gibbs free energy for the NR/organoclay nanocomposites can be determined from the Flory-Huggins equation [33]:

$$\Delta G = RT\left(\ln(1-\Phi_r) + \Phi_r + \chi\left(\phi_r^2\right)\right) \tag{5}$$

and from the statistical theory of rubber elasticity, ΔS can be obtained from ΔG=-TΔS, which assumes that no change in the internal energy of the networks occurs upon stretching.

Both thermodynamical parameters, *ΔS* and *ΔG*, of the studied materials are reported in Table 3. It must be noted that in presence of clay, *ΔG* decreases. However, a considerable increase of the energy is observed in the NR/organoclay nanocomposite. It is assumed that *ΔG* is closely related with the elastic behavior of the material, i.e, the organoclay nanocomposite shows a better elasticity than the other compositions. These results can be attributed to a better compatibility between the organosilicate and the elastomer. So, the rubber molecules can penetrate into the galleries more easily, giving rise to a process of exfoliation of the silicate layers. This exfoliation is the responsible of the noticeable increase of entropy loss as compared with clay composites.

These results are in concordance with those obtained by Mousa et al. [32] when analyzing the thermodynamical aspects of the SBR/silicate nanocomposites swollen in chloroform.

Thermal Analysis

The thermal properties of pure NR and NR/clay nanocomposites determined by TGA and DSC are summarized in Table 4.

Table 4. Thermal Properties of the Studied Materials

	TGA	DSC			
	Degradation peak, °C	t_{50}, min	t_{90}, min	ΔH_c (J/g)	T_g, °C
NR	382.9	10.81	23.00	9.20	-62.0
NR/clay	385.1	8.50	21.90	11.41	-60.4
NR/organoclay	393.1	1.71	6.46	19.61	-57.4

It can be deduced that the incorporation of clay hardly affects to the thermal stability of the natural rubber. These results confirm the formation of a conventional composite at a microscopic scale, where the polymer chains are not intercalated into the galleries of the silicate. However, when the organoclay is added to the NR a slight displacement of the degradation peak to higher temperatures is appreciated. This suggests that the thermal stability of the system is enhanced due to the formation of a composite at a nanoscale, where the polymer chains penetrate into the galleries of the clay, giving rise to an exfoliation of the silicate nanolayers. The clay nanolayers prevent out-diffusion of the volatile decomposition products [34].

DSC experiments were performed in isothermal and dynamic modes. The effect of the incorporation of the clay on the vulcanization reaction of natural rubber was analyzed under isothermal conditions. The DSC cure isotherms curves of pure NR and its composites at 160 °C, are shown in Figure 11. By integrating these curves, induction time, t_{50} and t_{90} have been obtained as tabulated in Table 4. From these results, it can be deduced that the curing time of the clay/NR composites slightly decreases as compared with the unfilled NR. However, in the case of NR/organoclay nanocomposite the vulcanization reaction is sensibly accelerated, showing a marked decrease in the curing times. These results are in concordance with those obtained from Monsanto measurements and support the strong assumption that the organoclay accelerates the NR vulcanization, mainly due to the amine groups present in the nanosilicate structure. In addition, the heat of reaction involved during the vulcanization under isothermal conditions increased in the presence of the organoclay. The obtained results are compiled in Table 4. This change in the heat of vulcanization suggests a higher crosslinks number on NR in the presence of the organoclay, as it was previously deduced from Monsanto measurements and crosslinking density analysis. Moreover, in order to analyze the effect of the organoclay on the elastomer glass transition temperature (T_g), a dynamic scan was performed. Temperature program was run from -100 to 0 °C at a heating rate of 20 °C/min under nitrogen atmosphere. The DSC thermograms for NR, NR/clay composite and NR/organoclay nanocomposite are shown in Figure 12. It can be seen that NR exhibits an endothermic peak at –62.0 °C whereas the T_g of NR/organoclay nanocomposite is about –57.4 °C. In the NR/organoclay nanocomposites, the mobility of NR chains is restricted by the saponite layers, giving rise to a slight increase of the nanocomposites T_g. This can be only due to the confinement of the elastomer chains within the silicate layers with a restriction in the mobility of the polymer chains.

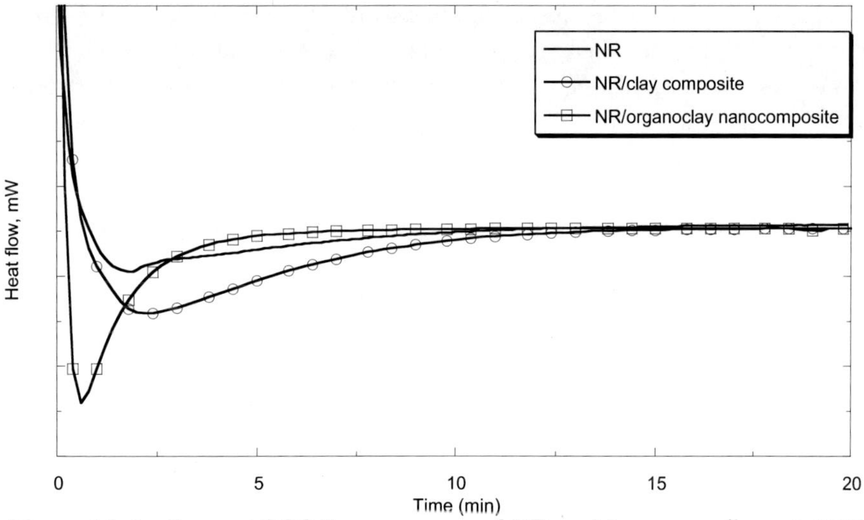

Figure 11. Isothermal DSC thermograms of NR and its composites, at 160 °C

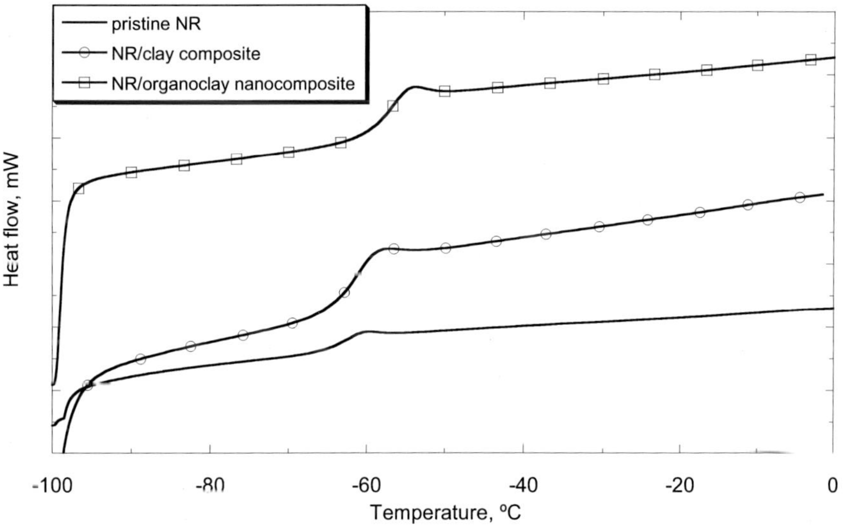

Figure 12. Determination of Tg of the studied materials by dynamic DSC thermograms

Mechanical Properties

The mechanical properties of the composites are reported in Table 5. The tensile properties are given in terms of the modulus at different strains (100, 300 and 500%), the strength and elongation at break. The low reinforcing effect of unmodified saponite is evident. A poor compatibility between the clay and the matrix (formation of a conventional composite at micro scale) is expected. A marked increase on the mechanical properties is observed for the organoclay as filler. Increments of above 350 % in the strength are obtained. The effect of the organoclay on the stiffness is more evident when measured at higher strains (increments of 191, 224 and 274% on the modulus are observed at 100, 300 and 500% elongations, respectively). In fact, the reinforcing effect of a filler is more noticeable at high elongations when it is perfectly dispersed in the matrix since the breakage depends on the amount of weak spots or inhomogeneities in the vulcanized rubber (35). Improved hardness and abrasion resistance are also in concordance with tensile results. It is important to note that the elastic characteristics of the NR are maintained in presence of the organoclay as deduced from the rebound resilience and compression set measurements.

Table 5. Mechanical Properties of the Studied Compounds

	NR	NR/clay (10 phr)	NR/organoclay (10 phr)	NR/c. black (10 phr)	NR/c. black (40 phr)
Modulus 100%, MPa	0.59	0.53	1.72	0.83	1.60
Modulus 300%, MPa	1.33	1.38	4.31	2.53	5.52
Modulus 500%, MPa	2.60	2.90	9.73	—	—
Max. Strength, MPa	4.25	3.60	15.0	4.93	10.3
Elongat at break, %	> 700	555	> 700	464	434
Hardness, shore A	28.8	20.7	43.5	30.5	38.3
Resilience, %	63.0	58.0	62.5	58.5	50.5
Compression set,%	17.5	27.9	22.4	28.7	42.8
Abrasion loss, mm^3	286.2	—	217.5	282.0	199.3
Density, g/cm^3	0.975	1.030	1.004	1.014	1.081

When comparing the organoclay with carbon black as fillers for NR, it is observed that at similar filler content the reinforcing effect of the organoclay is more noticeable. As deduced from Table 5, it is necessary to add 40 phr carbon black to obtain similar mechanical properties to the composite with 10 phr organoclay. However, high contents of carbon black give rise to a marked loss in the elastic behaviour of the NR composite.

Conclusions

Rubber/exfoliated clay nanocomposites are obtained with layered silicates intercalated by exchange ion reaction with quaternary ammonium salts by co-vulcanization process. In these materials, the silicate nanolayers were exfoliated and uniformly dispersed in the polymer matrix as deduced from X-ray diffractograms. The exfoliated forms of the silicate nanolayers in the polymer provide effective reinforcement for natural rubber. In fact, the organoclay behaves as an effective reinforcing agent, showing a stronger reinforcing effect than carbon black while retaining the elasticity of the elastomer. That is, only 10 phr of the organoclay are enough to obtain a similar mechanical behaviour to the compound with 40 phr of carbon black.

The obtained results suggest the possibility of substituting carbon black by white fillers, in particular an octadecylamine-modified saponite as reinforcement of natural rubber.

ACKNOWLEDGEMENTS

The authors wish to thank the CICyT, MAT 2001-1634, for financial support and Dr. López-Manchado for the concession of a Ramón y Cajal contract (MCyT).

REFERENCES

[1] LeBaron, P.C. Wang, Z. and Pinnavaia, T.G., *Appl. Clay Sci., 15*, 11-30 (1999).
[2] Giannelis, E.P. Krishamoorti, R. and Manias, E., *Advances in Polymer Science, 138* 107-147 (1999).
[3] Kojima, Y. Usuki, A. Kawasumi, M. Okada, A. Kurauchi, T. and Kamigaito, O., *J. Polym. Sci.: Part A: Polym. Chem., 31* 983-986 (1993).
[4] Yano, K. Uzuki, A. Okada, A. Kurauchi, T. and Kamigaito, O., *J. Polym. Sci.: Part A : Polym. Chem., 31* 2493-2498 (1993).
[5] Vaia, R.A. and Giannelis, E.P., *Macromolecules, 30* 7990-7999 (1997).
[6] Vaia, R.A. and Giannelis, E.P. *Macromolecules, 30* 8000-8009 (1997).
[7] Balazs, A.C. Singh, C. and Zhulina, E., Macromolecules *31* 8370-8381 (1998).
[8] Messersmith, P.B. and Giannelis, E.P., *J. Polym. Sci.: Part A: Polym. Chem., 33* 1047-1057 (1995) .
[9] Kojima, Y. Usuki, A. Kawasumi, M. Okada, A. Fukushima, Y. Kurauchi, T. and Kamigaito, O., *J. Appl. Polym. Sci., 49* 1259 (1993).
[10] Burnside, S.D. and Giannelis, E.P. *Chem. Mater., 7* 1597 (1995).
[11] Lee, J.D. Takekoshi, T. and Giannelis, E.P., *Mat. Res. Soc. Symp. Proc., 457* 513 (1997).
[12] Gilman, J.W. Kashiwagi, T. Lichetenhan, J.D. Giannelis, E.P. and Manias,E., 6th European Meeting on Fire Retardancy of Polymeric Materials, Lille, France, September, 24, (1997).
[13] Lee, J.D. and Giannelis, E.P., *Polymer Preprints, 38* 688 (1997).
[14] Gilman, J.W. Kashiwagi, and T. Lichetenhan, J.D., *SAMPE Journal*, *33* 40 (1997).
[15] "Nanocomposites New Low-Cost, High Strength Materials for Automotive Parts", National Institutes of Technology, *ATP Project*, 97-02-0047, (1997).
[16] Pinnavaia, T.J., *Science, 220* 365 (1983).
[17] Aranda, P. and Ruiz-Hitzky E., *Chem. Mater., 4* 1395-1403 (1992).
[18] Greenland, D.J., *J. Colloid Sci., 18* 647-664 (1963).
[19] Okada, A. Kawasumi, M. Usuki, A. Kojima, Y. Kurauchi, T. and Kamigaito, O., *Mater. Res. Soc. Proc., 171* 45-50 (1990).
[20] Blumstein, A., *J. Polym. Sci.; Part A: 3* 2665-2673 (1965).
[21] Krishnamoorti, R. Vaia, R.A. and Giannelis, E.P., *Chem. Mater., 8* 1728-1734 (1996).
[22] Lan, T. Kaviratna, P.D. and Pinnavaia, T. J., *Chem. Mater, 7*, 2144-2150 (1995).
[23] Lagaly, G., *Solis State Ionics, 22* 43-51 (1986).
[24] Messersmith, P.B. and Giannelis, E.P., *Chem. Mater., 6* 1719-1725 (1994).
[25] Theng, B.K.G., Formation and Properties of clay-polymer complexes, Elsevier, Amsterdam, p. 133 (1979).
[26] Vaia, R.A. Ishii, H. and Giannelis, E.P., *Chem. Mater., 5* 1694-1696 (1993).

[27] Vaia, R.A. Jandt, K.D. Kramer, E.J. and Giannelis, E. P., *Macromolecules*, *28* 8080-8085 (1995).

[28] Vaia, R.A. Jandt, K.D. Kramer, E. J. and Giannelis, E.P., *Chem. Mater*, *8* 2628-2635 (1996).

[29] López-Manchado, M.A. Herrero, B. and Arroyo, M., *Polymer International*, *52* 1070-1077 (2003).

[30] Arroyo, M., López-Manchado, M.A. and Herrero, B., Polymer, *44* 2447-2453 (2003).

[31] Joly, S., Garnaud, R., Ollitrault, R. and Bokobza, L., Chem. Mater, *14*, 4202-4208 (2002).

[32] Mousa, A. and Karger-Kocsis, J., *Macromol. Mater. Engng., 286*, 260 2001.

[33] Flory, P.J., in "Principle of Polymer Chemistry", Cornell University, Ithaca, New York, (1953).

[34] Chen, G. Lin, S. Chen, S. and Qi, Z, *Macromol. Chem. Phys.*, *202* 1189 (2001).

[35] Noordermeer, J.W.M. and Wilms, M.J.M., *Kautsch. Gummi Kunstst., 44*, 679 (1991).

INDEX

D

E

F

G

H

I

K

L

M

N

O

P

R